P9-EDS-879

Of Dikes and Windmills

Of Dikes and Windmills

Written and illustrated by

Peter Spier

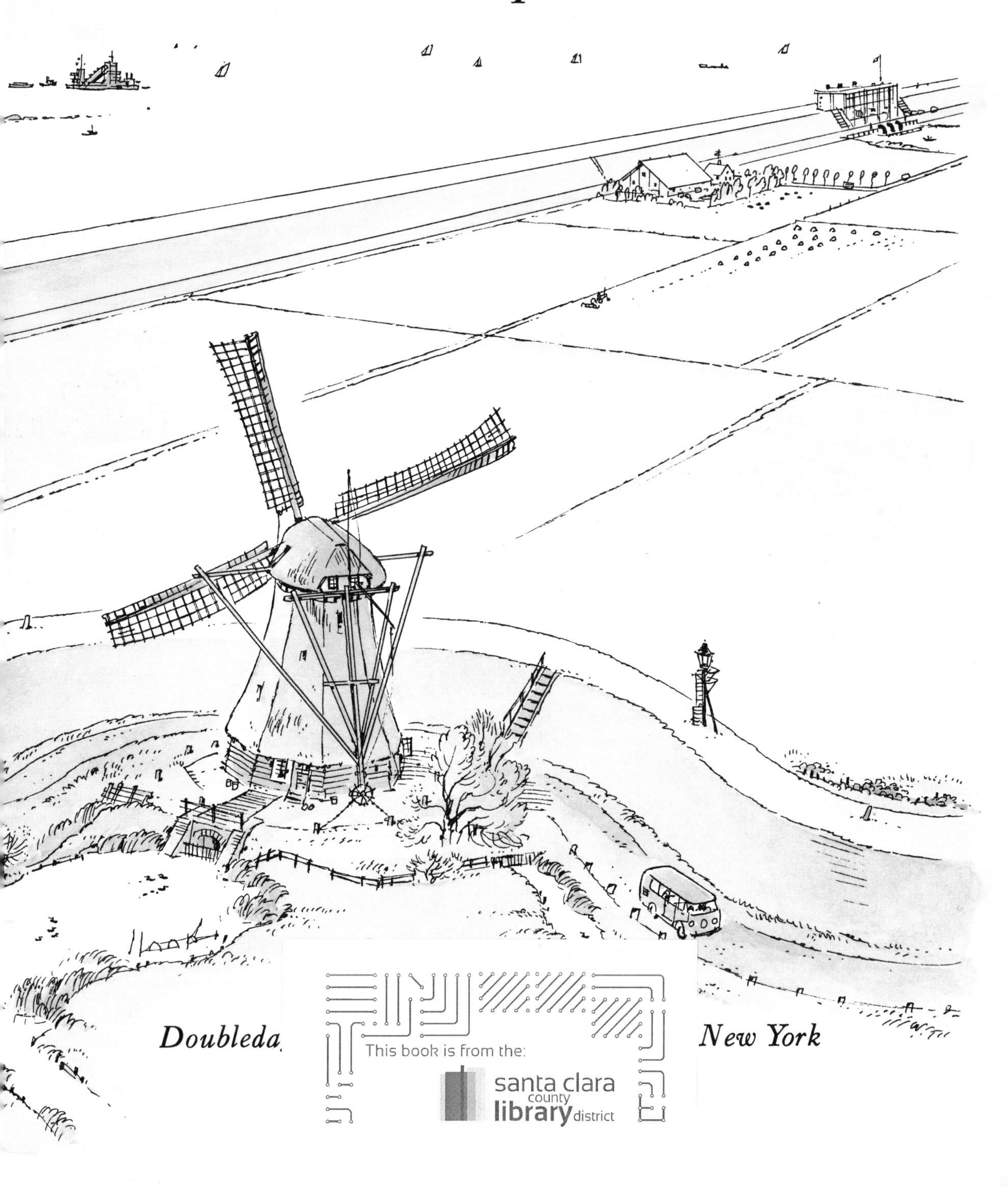

Doubleda[illegible] New York

Grateful acknowledgment is made for the use of the following copyrighted material: "Terpen Map" (adapted) from *De Dijken.* Used with permission of De Bezige Bij. Illustrations (adapted) from *Windmolens.* Used with permission of Uitgeverij Broekman & De Meris n.v. Illustrations (adapted) from *The Dutch Windmill* by F. Stokhuyzen. Used with permission of Van Dishoeck-Van Holkema & Warendorf n.v. Adapted from Aerial View KLM Aerocarto n.v. Used with permission of KLM Aerocarto n.v. Illustration from "Vijf Eeuwen Polderbemaling" from *Land & Water.* Used with permission of Ministerie van Verkeer en Waterstaat. Map (adapted) from *Dredge, Dike End Reclaim* by Dr. J. van Veen. Used with permission of Martinus Nijhoff. Illustrations (adapted) from *Holland and the DeltaPlan* by J. S. Lingsma. Used with permission of Rotterdam University Press. Excerpts from *De Molen In Ons Volksleven* by A. Bicker-Caarten. Used with permission of A. W. Sijthoff's Uitgeversmaatschappij n.v. Map (adapted) from *Tussen Afsluitdammen en Deltadijken* Vol. II. Used with permission of M. H. Wilderom.

Library of Congress Catalog Card Number 72-78028. Printed in the United States of America.

First Edition

To my parents

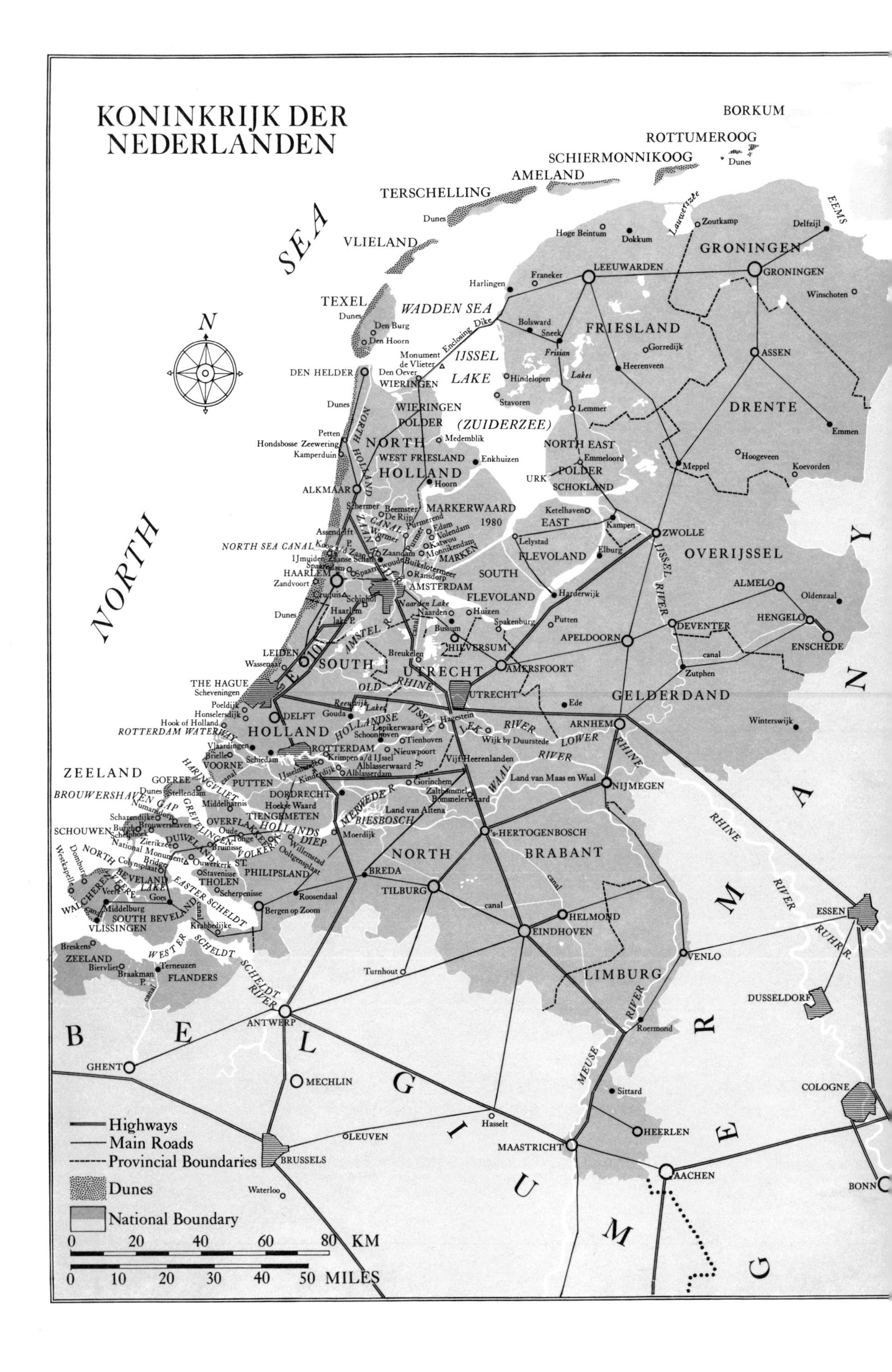
KONINKRIJK DER NEDERLANDEN
BORKUM
ROTTUMEROOG
SCHIERMONNIKOOG
AMELAND
TERSCHELLING
VLIELAND
TEXEL
Dunes
NORTH SEA
WADDEN SEA
Den Burg
Den Hoorn
DEN HELDER
Den Oever
WIERINGEN
Monument de Vlieter
Enclosing Dike
IJSSEL LAKE
(ZUIDERZEE)
Hoge Beintum
Dokkum
Lauwerszee
Zoutkamp
Delfzijl
EEMS
GRONINGEN
Winschoten
Harlingen
Franeker
LEEUWARDEN
Bolsward
Sneek
FRIESLAND
Gorredijk
Frisian Lakes
Heerenveen
Hindelopen
Stavoren
Lemmer
ASSEN
DRENTE
Emmen
WIERINGEN POLDER
Petten
Hondsbosse Zeewering
Kamperduin
NORTH HOLLAND
Medemblik
WEST FRIESLAND
Enkhuizen
Hoorn
ALKMAAR
NORTH EAST POLDER
Emmeloord
URK
SCHOKLAND
Meppel
Hoogeveen
Koevorden
Schermer
Beemster
De Rijp
Purmerend
Edam
Volendam
MARKERWAARD 1980
Ketelhaven
EAST FLEVOLAND
Lelystad
Kampen
ZWOLLE
Elburg
OVERIJSSEL
NORTH SEA CANAL
IJmuiden
Zaandam
Monnikendam
MARKEN
HAARLEM
Zandvoort
Spaarndam
AMSTERDAM
SOUTH FLEVOLAND
Harderwijk
ALMELO
Oldenzaal
HENGELO
ENSCHEDE
Cruquius
Schiphol
Haarlem Lake
Naarden Lake
Naarden
Huizen
Bussum
Spakenburg
Putten
DEVENTER
APELDOORN
LEIDEN
Wassenaar
E 10
SOUTH HOLLAND
AMSTEL R.
Breukelen
HILVERSUM
AMERSFOORT
canal
Zutphen
UTRECHT
THE HAGUE
Scheveningen
Poeldijk
Honselersdijk
Hook of Holland
ROTTERDAM WATERWAY
DELFT
Gouda
OLD RHINE
Reeuwijk Lakes
HOLLANDSE IJSSEL
Hagestein
LEK RIVER
Ede
GELDERLAND
Winterswijk
ARNHEM
LOWER RHINE
Wijk by Duurstede
Lopikerwaard
Schoonhoven
Tienhoven
Nieuwpoort
Vlaardingen
Brielle
VOORNE
Schiedam
ROTTERDAM
Krimpen a/d IJssel
Alblasserwaard
Alblasserdam
Vijf Heerenlanden
Land van Maas en Waal
NIJMEGEN
WAAL
ZEELAND
GOEREE
HARINGVLIET
Dunes
Stellendam
PUTTEN
DORDRECHT
Gorinchem
Zaltbommel
Bommelerwaard
BROUWERSHAVEN GAP
Middelharnis
Hoekse Waard
MERWEDE R.
Land van Altena
TIENGEMETEN
BIESBOSCH
Scharendijke
Brouwershaven
OVERFLAKKEE
HOLLANDS DIEP
Moerdijk
's-HERTOGENBOSCH
SCHOUWEN
Burgh
Zierikzee
DUIVELAND
GREVELINGEN
Bruinisse
VOLKERAK
Willemstad
Ooltgensplaat
Westkapelle
Domburg
NORTH BEVELAND
National Monument
Colynsplaat
Ouwerkerk
ST. PHILIPSLAND
NORTH BRABANT
BREDA
WALCHEREN
VEERE LAKE
Veere
Stavenisse
THOLEN
Scherpenisse
Goes
EASTER SCHELDT
Roosendaal
TILBURG
Middelburg
SOUTH BEVELAND
Bergen op Zoom
Krabbedijke
canal
HELMOND
VLISSINGEN
EINDHOVEN
Breskens
WESTER SCHELDT
ZEELAND FLANDERS
Biervliet
Terneuzen
Braakman P.
VENLO
LIMBURG
Turnhout
SCHELDT RIVER
ANTWERP
RHINE RIVER
ESSEN
RUHR R.
DUSSELDORF
Roermond
GERMANY
BELGIUM
GHENT
MECHLIN
MEUSE RIVER
Sittard
HEERLEN
COLOGNE
Hasselt
LEUVEN
MAASTRICHT
AACHEN
BRUSSELS
BONN
Waterloo
Highways
Main Roads
Provincial Boundaries
Dunes
National Boundary
0 20 40 60 80 KM
0 10 20 30 40 50 MILES
N

Foreword

"What's in a name?" asked Shakespeare. In the case of Holland, just about everything, for Holland means hollow land, and its official name, *Koninkrijk der Nederlanden* or Kingdom of the Netherlands, means the same thing. (The dictionary says: Nether: situated down or below, lower, under.) But why the two names, Holland and the Netherlands? In 1579, during the war of independence against Spain, seven provinces of the Netherlands (Holland, Friesland, Groningen, Overijssel, Utrecht, Gelderland, and Zeeland) formed a confederation and later called themselves "the Republic of the United Netherlands." Holland was the largest and richest of these seven United Provinces and her name has been commonly used for the whole country ever since.

Most nations are much larger: more than eleven Hollands could fit within the borders of Montana. Some nations—but not many—are more densely populated, for there are almost 13,000,000 Dutchmen. By contrast, the population of Montana is 705,000.

Holland's problems are much the same as those of most modern nations, and the Hollanders' worries and pleasures basically do not differ much from those of people anywhere else in the world. But what makes Holland so totally different from any other land on earth is that some 2000 years ago most of it simply was not there!

The French philosopher Descartes once said, "God made the world, but the Dutch made Holland."

This is the story of how they did it.

I

A leaden sky, a cold grim sea: one moment tranquil, the next a roaring mass of waves and flying foam, breaking on a shallow coast of tidal marshes, mudflats, and peat bog. Most of the time it rained. The only visible living creatures the circling, screaming seabirds searching for food and a few flapping silvery fish trapped in the dripping marshlands by the waning tide.

All summer long the sea built up this eerie coast, gently depositing sand and clay, but in winter, as if in anger, she destroyed her own work again. Man did not live here. Far inland, where bear, giant deer, and mammoth roamed the great forests, man was to be found, living in caves or in the most primitive shelters, clad in animal skins and hunting with flintheaded spears.

It was only in summer that man ventured down into the marshes to get eggs or to go fishing. They caught salmon and sturgeon in the wide river mouths; cod, shrimp, and herring in the surf of the restless sea. But when the wind began to blow, driving the waves higher and higher, man fled in great haste to the east, toward high ground and safety. This gloomy, uninviting place, belonging to neither land nor sea, lay scattered around the estuary of what we call the river Rhine.

It had all begun much earlier, countless thousands of years ago, when the Rhine flowed through Britain, which was then connected to the continent. The Thames was a tributary of the Rhine, and the Meuse reached the ocean far to the north.

Then it grew bitterly cold, for the ice ages had arrived, and enormous glaciers blocked the rivers with ice and sand. As a result, the low land bridge between Britain and the continent was transformed into a vast marshland. At the same time, the great quantities of sand pushed up by the creeping glaciers laid the foundations of present-day Holland. The highest ridges were in the east, now Gelderland, Drente, and Overijssel. To the west a long ridge stretched from today's Zeeland to the islands in the north.

But at the end of the most recent ice age, the Pleistocene epoch, the climate began to get warmer, a few degrees per century. The ice melted and the sea level rose hundreds of feet, covering everything except the highest points. This is how the North Sea was born and how Britain became an island.

Between the narrow ridge and the heights in the east now lay an enormous lagoon through which Rhine and Meuse reached the sea, carrying silt and clay into the lagoon for the next 100,000 years. The inland sea filled in and vegetation flourished. Then, over the centuries, it grew colder and colder. The area became a Siberia-like tundra—a vast, treeless plain. Forty thousand years later it gradually became warmer again. More melting ice raised the sea, and this time the approximate coastline of present-day Holland appeared.

At this point something happened that would change the face of the land forever: men arrived, probably from Central Europe. They first lived 18,000 years ago on the island Texel. Between 6000 and 4000 B.C. the area was permanently settled and 1000 years later there were some tens of thousands of inhabitants. They lived only on the natural heights and fearfully abandoned their meager fields to the sea in winter. The idea that it might be possible for them to fight back had not occurred to them yet. But it would before long!

The tribes that had settled in the west were called the Batavians and the Kaninefaten. Those that lived in today's Friesland were the Frisians. Friesland was settled between 500 and 400 B.C. Here nature had not been kind enough to provide any heights worth mentioning, so the Frisians began to throw up mounds that were just a bit higher than the sea at high tide. Upon these they built their huts and kept some cattle. At the foot of these mounds they cultivated small fields, but hightailed it to their *terpen*—as the mounds were and are still called—when the sea rose. (One of these mounds is a *terp.*)

The first tourist showed up in 325 B.C., shortly after the death of Alexander the Great. He was a Greek, Pytheas of Massilia (Marseilles), a mathematician, astronomer, and scientist of renown—although one may doubt the last. He went home with such utterly fantastic stories that most people refused to believe a word of them. He then proceeded to write a book about his experiences, which must have been the first travel guide to Western Europe. Pytheas wrote that he had seen "the lung of the sea far in the north, where water, ice and air mingle. It was the end of the earth." (I must, however, admit here that he did not exaggerate too much about the weather, which is still about the same.) "And there I saw the sea rise and fall with regularity!" He went on to explain this last interesting item as "the sea lung" of an enormous jellyfish. The sea lung legend is still to be found on the Shetland Islands and on Iceland, and is considered proof that Pytheas went that far north. It was not surprising that his readers back home regarded his science-fiction skeptically, for the tides in the Mediterranean are hardly noticeable, while the sea recedes for many miles on the mudflats of Holland at low tide. Still, it was through Pytheas that the civilized world of Greece and Rome knew of this part of the globe and his works earned him the sobriquet of "Humboldt of Antiquity." Which is, after all, better than nothing.

For the next 350 years, history ignored and forgot this soggy fringe on the edge of the world.

In 50 B.C. Julius Caesar completed the conquest of Gaul, and before long the Romans arrived in the Lowlands to guard the flanks of Gaul and Belgium against attacks from Germany. Serving with the Roman army a century later was Caius Plinius Secundus, whom we know as Pliny the Elder. To him we owe the best descriptions of what he called "the people dwelling on the islands of the Rhine." He wrote: "Here a miserable people live on high hills or mounds that they have made and on which they have built their huts. They are like sailors when the tide is high and like castaways when the waters have again retreated."

In the center of the lowlands lay what remained of the lagoon of old Lake Flevo, across which the Roman fleets sailed to reach their garrisons in northern Germany and on the Baltic. It must have been on one of these trips that Pliny first saw the Frisians, and it seems worth remembering that the sophisticated Pliny, who so obviously felt sorry about the fate to which nature had condemned the marsh dwellers, was destined to lose his own life at nature's hand in the eruption of the Vesuvius that buried Pompeii in 79 A.D.

Meanwhile, the Frisians began their terp building in earnest and continued to do so until well into the twelfth century. Altogether they constructed 1260 of them, and many can still be seen today rising up out of the level land, with a church or a lonely windswept farm perched on top. There are also many which cannot be seen because the old mound community grew into a village or town, spilled over the edges of

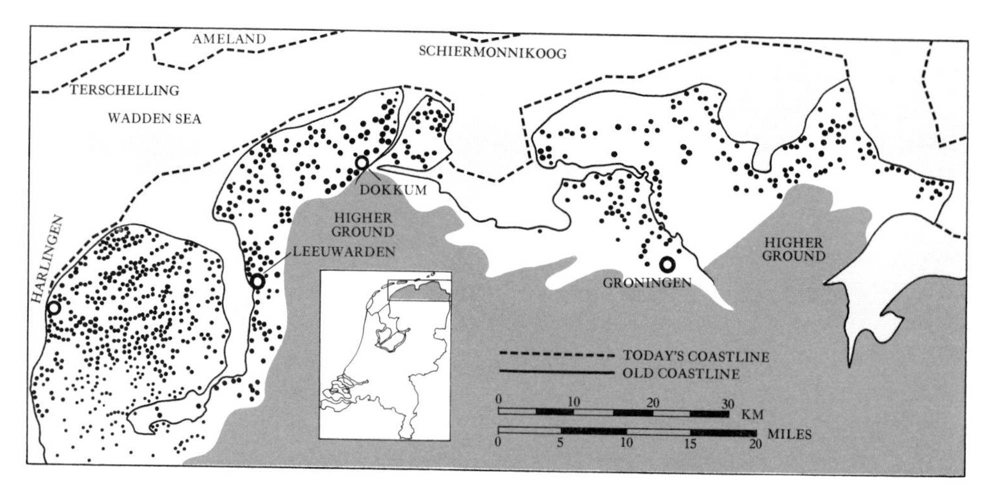

The terpen constructed along the coast of Friesland and Groningen by A.D. 600 Each dot represents one terp.

the old ancestral terp, and now hides it within its streets. Most of the terpen were small, but some grew into plateaus of forty acres that stood fully thirty feet above the ground. Today there is not a single terp left completely intact, for in later days the farmers began to dig into them. Don't blame them too much—you might have done the same. The terpen consisted of layer upon layer of clay, straw, and dung, and presented tempting mountains of the finest soil imaginable.

In 15 B.C. the Romans under General Drusus, a brother of Emperor Tiberius, completely occupied the Lowlands, and three years later the area became an imperial province of Rome. Promptly things began to move. The civilized newcomers introduced selective breeding methods that improved the herds, founded large, efficient estates that were run with the latest agricultural methods, and taught the natives that there were other edibles besides seagull eggs, tough old cows, and lots of fish. Lentils, radishes, cabbage, and plum trees were among the new crops that the Romans planted in the region, and they are an important part of the Dutch menu today.

But there was a far more important novelty that the Romans introduced: dikes! There were two reasons why dikes were necessary: the first was that the lands along the rivers were fantastically fertile, but had the disadvantage of being flooded by the swollen rivers in the spring. The second reason was that the legions needed dependable roads that were dry at all times. During the four centuries that the Romans remained in the lowlands the face of the land changed. Many river dikes were built. At their base appeared green pastures in which healthy herds of cattle grazed and rich crops were harvested. Forts and trading posts sprang up that became centers of enterprise and civilization in the near barbarian surroundings. Roman traders arrived with treasures: fine cloth, pottery, and jewelry. The Lowlands had become part of the world.

But in the coastal marshes things remained the same—the sea was master and attacked at will. The Frisians stayed on their mounds to which they kept patiently adding clay and stones to keep them strong, carrying the building materials from afar in willow baskets and bags of hide. They were an extremely independent people and did not like to pay taxes to the Romans. In 28 A.D. they rose in anger. Here is what Tacitus has to say about it:

"That year the Frisii, a nation beyond the Rhine, cast off peace, more because of rapacity than from their impatience of subjection. Drusus had imposed on them a moderate tribute, suitable to their limited resources, the furnishing of oxhides for military purposes. No one ever severely scrutinized the size or thickness till Olenius, a first rank Centurion, appointed to govern the Frisii, selected hides of wild bulls as the standard according to which they were to be paid."

He then continues to say that this would have been hard for anyone, but even more so for the Frisians whose terp-bred cattle were pretty scrawny creatures. The Frisians murdered the tax collectors and Olenius barely saved his skin by fleeing to the Roman fortress on Flevum, today's island, Vlieland. Now the revolt began in earnest and the Frisians inflicted heavy losses on the legions.

"Tiberius kept our losses a secret," writes Tacitus, "not wishing to entrust anyone with the war. Nor did the Senate care whether dishonor fell on the extreme frontiers of the empire."

Small terp. Sneek.

The Romans decided that the marshes were not worth the trouble after all and around 30 A.D. they retreated to the left bank of the Rhine. The Frisians of today are as independent as their ancestors and as stubborn. (Peter Stuyvesant was a Frisian and they called him "Stubborn Pete.") Their second language, next to Dutch, is a form of Gaelic. It is taught in their schools, books are written in it, and no one outside the province understands a single word of it.

With Rome's decline their legions marched away, in about 350 A.D. Lacking Roman know-how and guidance, civilization—which had never been more than skin deep—disappeared. The roads, forts, and trading posts lay deserted. After only a few years had passed there was little visible evidence that the Romans had ever been here. Gone were the sounds of progress, of wheels creaking under the weight of newly harvested grain, of construction, hammering, and of saws biting into wood. But the river dikes were there to stay.

A great, gloomy silence spread over the Lowlands. It lasted almost 400 years.

Hoge Beintum terp completed in the 12th century rises 36 feet above the endless flat meadows and is one of the highest in Friesland. However, it shared the fate of all others. Of the original 25 acres only a fraction remains. A narrow brick road leads up one side and down the other, passing through a "village" consisting of an early medieval church and three homes. In 1900 scientific excavations were begun and among countless objects from all periods several skeletons that had been buried in hollowed-out logs were found. Hoge Beintum no longer protects man but, as a historic monument, is protected by man instead.

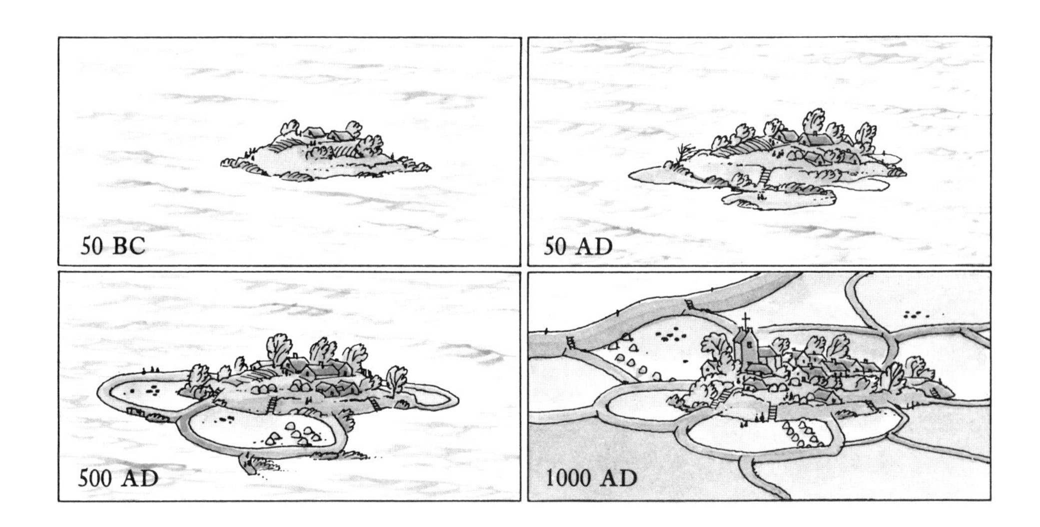

II

With the dawn of the Dark Ages the mound dwellers fought back: they began building dikes. Their weapon was the spade; their ammunition sand and clay; their ally was the summer; and their enemy—as always—was the sea.

As the centuries passed, the ground surrounding the terpen grew slowly higher with silt and it was around these fields, which until that time could be tilled in the summer only, that the first sea dikes were built. This area outside the mound was called a *polle*—in Frisian it is still known as a *pol*—and it is the root of the word *polder*. A polder is simply a low-lying piece of land reclaimed from the water and protected by dikes. Around these first polders, nestled against the terp, the sea added fresh silt, which was then diked in. In this manner new polders were added all the time. But, as always, there was a problem: it was impossible to keep them really dry, for ground water and the rain that accumulated inside had no way to get out.

Around the year 800 a new tool was added to the meager arsenal of the mound dwellers: the sluices—two doors that were pushed open by the pressure of the water in the polder when the tide was low, but that closed tightly when the water from outside came back at high tide. Like the dikes, these water locks were not a Dutch invention; similar ones had been used for thousands of years in Mesopotamia and in Egypt. Still, there was always danger and change, for the sea was forever demolishing what man had built up so painstakingly out of sand and clay.

It was a constant war, waged without a truce or even a distant glimmer of hope for peace, and the people did not dare leave their heights. "Keep the peace toward your neighbors and do everything which is decent and right," said the oldest Frisian law, "then heighten and strengthen the dikes!"

After the departure of the Romans, the Lowlands came under the rule of the Franks, becoming a part of Charlemagne's (742–814) Holy Roman Empire. Among Charlemagne's many accomplishments, his enlightened laws are especially well remembered.

While the other tribes had to contribute soldiers to his army, the Frisians were granted special laws—the *Lex Frisionum*—one of which stated that only they were not required to serve away from home. If they were not around when the sea attacked their land, there would be no land for them to go home to.

The Frisians were a scrappy lot and when they were not fighting the sea they bashed each other over the head. But when a dike was threatened they threw down their arms, forgot the quarrel, and rushed together to the endangered spot. This was called the "dike peace." The man who dared to break it or refused to work on the dikes was condemned to death and was usually buried alive in the breach in the dike. However brutal, the system seems to have worked, for around the year 1000 Friesland was diked in! The job had taken 300 years.

Every man had to take care of the dike section protecting his land and keep it in perfect shape. The law of the land became "Dike or Leave." The man unable to keep his dike in top condition was forced to put his spade in the dike, which meant, "I give up." He was forced to leave his land and home, which then came into the possession of the younger or stronger man who pulled that spade out of the ground and repaired the dike. This may seem harsh, but one weak spot, one broken dike in the system, could start a chain reaction as polder after polder flooded, with results that you can easily imagine.

By the way, if you ever meet a Mynheer Terpstra, Wierda of Kleiberg (Claymound), you will know where his great-great-(and here follows a lot more greats) grandfather came from. From now on you may smile knowingly if you are introduced to Mr. Dykstra, Mr. Dykmans, Mr. van der Pol or Mr. Poldermans. The Dutch telephone books are full of them!

And so the people began to enjoy some modest prosperity, tilling their land and fishing on the wet side of the dikes. During the eighth and ninth centuries other fishermen had come to the Lowlands dressed in cassocks, clutching a crozier and fishing for souls: the first Christian mis-

Radbod's often restored castle at Medemblik, now used for official functions and exhibits. After 1300 the castle played a minor tactical role in the wars of that time.

sionaries. They had an especially hard time converting the stubborn Frisians, who for many years showed no interest at all. But interest and conversion are two altogether different matters. In 754 Bonifacius (an Englishman) arrived to give the heathen another chance to save their immortal souls.

Radbod, King of the Frisians, who did not feel kindly disposed toward missionaries in general because experience had shown him that his converted subjects tended to be somewhat less than loyal to their heathen king, ordered Bonifacius killed. The Frisians did not have to be told twice and immediately massacred Bonifacius and his companions near Dokkum. The church leaders were not discouraged. They canonized Saint Bonifacius (Saint Boniface), and sent new missionaries to Radbod's court. These missionaries made him see the error of his ways and Radbod decided to become a Christian.

The priests were about to baptize the kneeling king, when he interrupted the proceedings with one last question: "Will I go to heaven when I die a Christian?" The missionaries fervently assured him that he would.

"Will I meet my ancestors there as well?" He was then informed that unfortunately this was entirely out of the question in view of the fact that they had died heathen. "In that case I am not interested in becoming a Christian either!" said Radbod, getting up. And that was that.

Even so, over the years the population was converted and the new monasteries and abbeys became centers of culture and initiative, like the Roman forts of so long ago. Thus order reigned once again.

It was not only in the north that dikes appeared. In the south, where the long row of sand dunes protecting Holland's flank ended, lay the islands of Zeeland, surrounded by a maze of rivers, deep channels, gullies, and shifting sand banks. In 250 B.C. there had been dense forests and high sand dunes on Walcheren Island, but the rising sea had forced the inhabitants out. They had returned in 800 A.D., and like the Frisians, had made their home on terpen (only here they were called *wierden*) and on the few dunes left. Here in the south there was an additional danger to deal with: the big rivers. All summer long the rivers flowed serenely in wide, graceful bends through the lush green fields. But in spring they ran amuck, overflowing with melted snow from the Alps, and swept away trees, homes, and cattle.

Dike building in Zeeland began in the year 1000. Slowly the dikes grew: gigantic, benevolent, green serpents uncoiling foot by foot. Behind their increasing security more people settled down, building new polders and cultivating more land on which fat cattle grazed. The old mound-dwelling communities grew into villages and these, with the passing of time, became small towns.

And so—against all odds—a pattern emerged in the Dutch provinces, fragile and insecure. Over the years whole parts of the work would be undone, wiped out, washed away; the back-breaking labor of centuries wrecked in hours by the fury of the water. But the people hung on, never discouraged, never leaving; repairing the damage, and rebuilding their dikes higher, stronger, and longer. Between the Dutch and the sea it was a never-ending process of give-and-take, but in the long run the Dutch took more than they gave. Just look at today's map of Holland!

The first dikes were just dams thrown up out of sand and clay. The same thing happened to them that happens to a sand castle built on the beach when the first little wave gently laps at its base. However, the Dutch soon learned that it was better to bury twigs in the base of the dike and heap more twigs along the water's edge. They discovered that the roots of plants and grasses planted on the dike held the soil together and that a coating of heavy clay improved the resistance of their sea walls. Also of great importance was the shape of the dike: a sea dike had to slope gradually down toward the water. Thus the waves lost much

THE CHANGING SHAPE

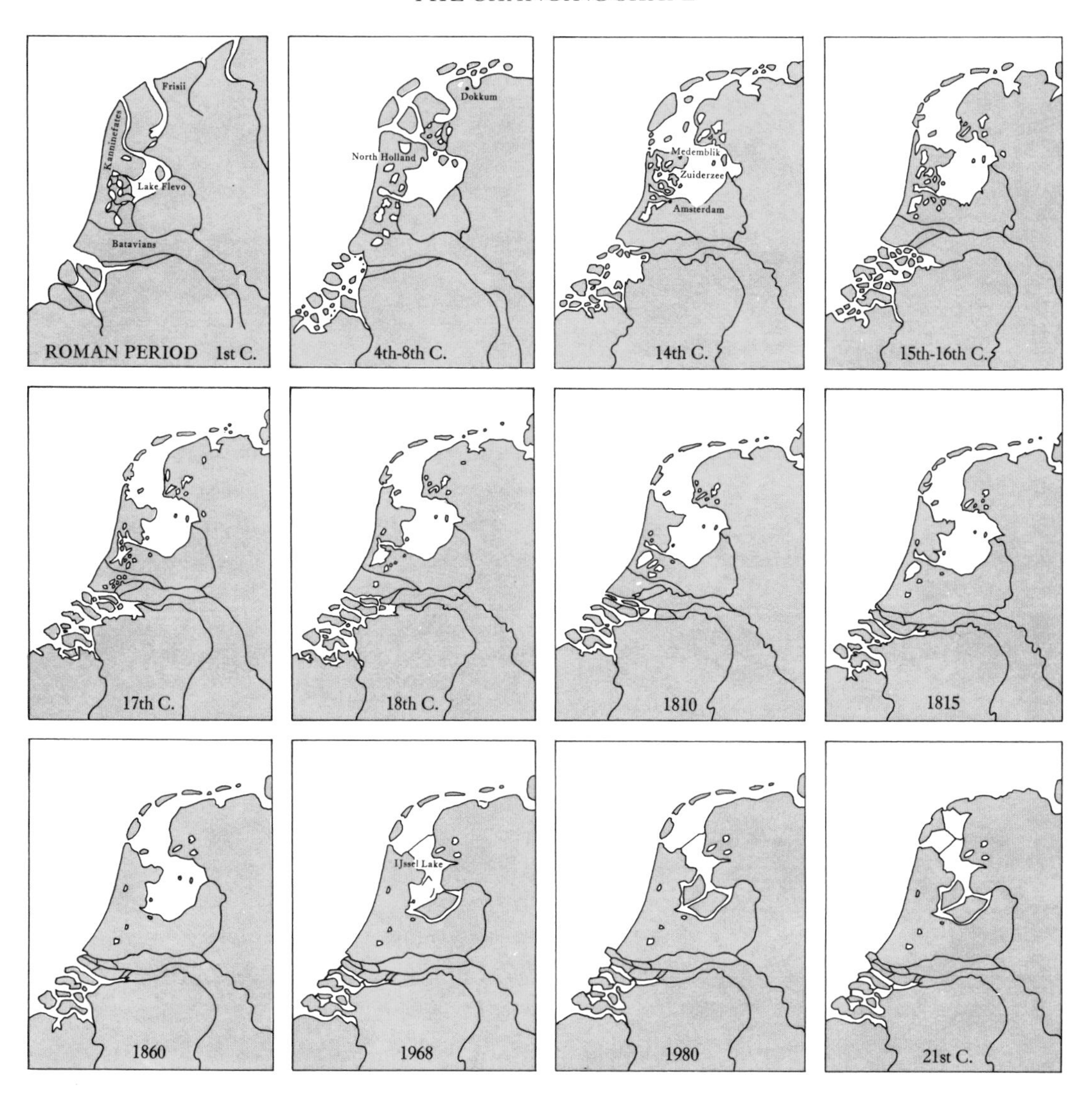

A: What Holland would look like if man had not been at work there. B: The area protected by more than 2000 miles of dunes and sea and river dikes. C: Since the year 1200 the Dutch have reclaimed close to 1,700,000 acres from the sea.

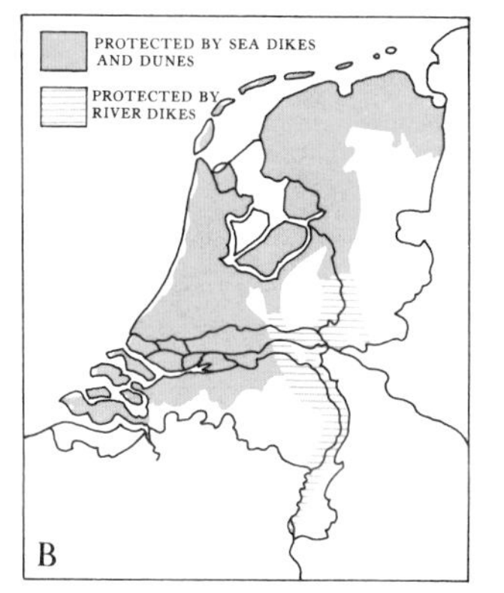

of their momentum by the time they reached the base of the dike.

Across Flevo Lake lay West Friesland and North Holland; here different dikes were developed. The side of the dike facing the sea rose almost vertically out of the water and was coated right up to the crown with a mixture of sand, clay, and seaweed. The seaweed fermented and eventually transformed the whole into a rock-hard "armor belt," sometimes up to twenty feet thick, that could withstand the pounding of the waves. These weed dikes were being built for over 800 years—until the 1850s.

The type of dike used depended as much on local requirements as on the available materials. When there was no seaweed, reeds were substituted. These did not harden the "frosting" like the weeds did and had to be replaced every five or six years, a very costly procedure. To make a reed dike last as long as possible, it was often protected by long rows of poles placed some distance from the dike so that the force of the waves had been broken by the time they reached the dike itself. These later evolved into pole dikes.

One day in 1282 an unknown carpenter and his helpers began to construct an odd-looking building on the edge of a polder. It was fairly tall and had a strange slatted cross mounted near the roof. Hidden inside was a large wooden wheel with wooden troughs set between the rims. The wheel was half in and half out of the water and was connected to the cross by a simple system of heavy gears made with wooden pegs. When the carpenters were finished, they tied long strips of sailcloth to the slatted wings. The wind began to blow against the sails and the wings began to turn slowly, and so did the scooped wheel inside. It lifted the water from inside the polder some four feet up and threw it across the dike where it ran off. That carpenter probably rubbed his hands, slapped his helpers on their backs, and said, "*Verdorie,* it works!" but it seems unlikely that he realized he had built the machine that would make—and keep—Holland dry. This was Holland's first water-pumping windmill, the ancestor of a long and distinguished line. It rattled, clanked, and creaked. It was not too efficient, but it worked! Each new one built would be a little better and a little bigger than the one before. They would pump night and day—century after century—whenever there was enough wind to make their vanes go around. They would never stop—and have not to this day.

Although the windmill has come to be the symbol of Holland, I'm sorry to report that it, too, was not a Dutch, but, in all likelihood, an Arab invention. Returning Crusaders had seen them at work in the Middle East where they were used to lift water from the rivers onto the tilled fields. It cannot have been long before someone got the idea that it would also work the other way around.

The early mills were mostly gristmills. One is mentioned in 1299. On the spot where it was built in North Brabant there has stood a mill ever since.

The land on which the first windmills were built belonged to the nobility. In fact, all the land belonged to the nobility, whether a count, duke, or a mere lowly lord. When the landowner gave his permission to construct a mill, the miller received his "wind letter." But this was by no means all, for a nobleman knew when he was on to a profitable thing, and usually made the most of the occasion. He was not only paid rent for the land, but he also claimed the wind that blew over it.

The miller thus had to "lease" the wind as well for a nominal sum. It was a bargain, however, because this "wind right" included "the eternal privilege to the unobstructed wind." This meant that no trees could be planted or houses built close to the mill. There was a good reason for this: a disturbed or interrupted flow of the wind can cause a mill to wobble or to lose its balance. Once that happens, a mill can no longer be controlled and can easily destroy itself like a washing machine spinning with the whole load on one side of the drum. These wind rights still exist today. The miller no longer has to buy the wind. This custom was abolished in the late eighteenth century at the time of the French Revolution, but the building restrictions around the mill have not changed:

"Article 1. It is prohibited—without the required permission—to erect a building or construction of a height exceeding 12 feet, within a distance of 150 feet of a drainage windmill, or to plant trees within 100 feet of a mill.

"Article 2. It is unlawful to . . ."

And so the dreary laws continue, page after page.

The landlord also insisted on being paid a certain percentage of all the wheat or corn ground in "his" mill. It was usual in those days for people to grind their own flour at home. But when a nobleman was short of money, he forbade home-grinding and thereby forced his tenants to use his mill. This "forced milling," too, was discontinued after 1792.

There were, however, exceptions to the rule: on May 24, 1668, the Baron of Wassenaer granted Jan van Wouw the right to build a gristmill at his own expense in return for "an annual recognition of 60 guilders and two pairs of capons." That mill, by the way, is still in use today, although no capons have changed hands since 1798!

The Baron of Wassenaer also had other mills on his lands and for these the millers paid him the customary "wind money." One day the baron raised the price to 100 guilders per annum. At a period when one of the mills was very busy, the wind died down and things literally ground to a halt. The baron happened to pass the mill just then and the miller asked him respectfully to provide some wind at his earliest convenience. "How could I possibly do that?" asked the flabbergasted nobleman. "But, sir, that's what I've been paying you for!" said the miller.

After the abolition of wind rights and forced milling, the millers still had to pay taxes; but they were now paid to the government and were based on the amounts of flour produced.

The new laws were enforced by customs officers who visited the mills at unexpected times. The millers did not like this one bit and ingeniously constructed large, secret compartments in their mills—called "smuggle boxes"—which could be quickly filled, thereby avoiding taxation on considerable quantities of flour.

Millers were required to keep precise accounts in their "mill book" as to the exact amounts that had been ground, both for taxation and to avoid unpleasantness with their customers, the farmers. But with the new and detested taxation, millers devised their own bookkeeping codes which no one else could read, like the ones shown below.

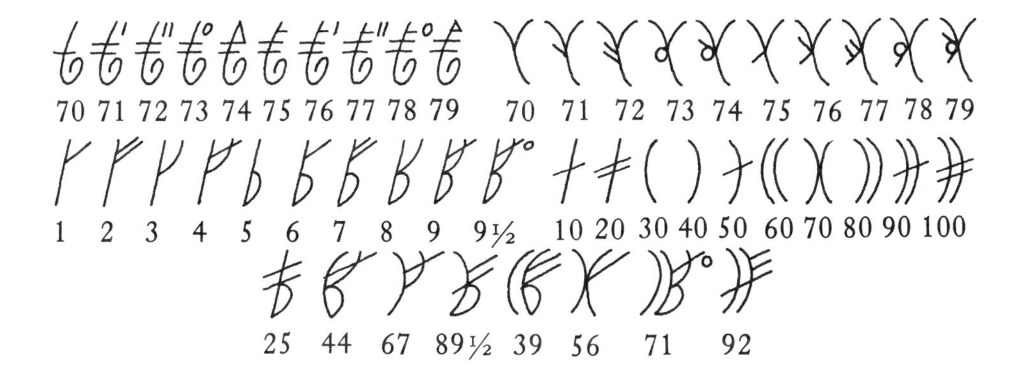

Often gristmillers would let their mills work during the day even if there was nothing to be ground, thereby creating the impression that they were as busy as could be. For if the farmers suspected otherwise it might influence the price they were willing to pay.

Still, since the earliest days there have been "poor people's mills." These were gristmills which were the property of monasteries or churches, and later the Boards of Regents of the Alms and Poorhouses. The mills

Teamwork: the mill in the foreground stands in the polder and lifts polderwater into the waterway across the dike, from where the second mill in turn pumps it to a higher level. The heavy beam supported by braces is the tail pole anchored to the revolving cap. When the wind shifts, the miller will attach a chain from the capstan to the posts and crank the wheel until the vanes face the wind. The living room floor is on ground level, the small window above dimly lights the bedroom floor.

were worked by monks or hired millers, and sometimes by "hedge millers," who had no mill of their own but filled in at other people's mills when needed. The profit made in the "poor mill" was spent on the poor of the community. A childless miller often willed his mill to the poor, and today there are still five poor mills active in the Netherlands.

There was only one thing wrong with the first windmills: they were static. More often than not, the wind blew out of the southwest, so the mills were built facing in that direction. As a result, they could only operate when the wind blew from exactly that point of the compass: straight at them. They were like ships able to sail in one direction only. The invention of the revolving mill around 1526 remedied this defect. Now the mill pivoted on a great central axle and the miller could crank the whole mill around to face the wind. If a Dutchman tells you to be careful or *je krygt de wind van voren* (you'll face the wind), he's telling you to watch out, or you'll have to "face the music." Still later, when the mills grew larger, the method was refined so that only the top, to which the wings were attached, turned. In any case, the windmill had come of age and could be worked no matter where the wind blew. Cautious Dutchmen always wait to take a decision until they've found out *uit welke hoek the wind waait* (out of which corner the wind is blowing).

Twenty-seven years after the first pumping mill was built, others were hard at work all over the land, multiplying like rabbits. At least that's how the Dutch put it. The exact number of mills built in those early days is not known. But it may give you a rough idea to know that Amsterdam had nine windmills in 1544 and a few years later twelve. The city of Brugge—today in Belgium—had twenty-five mills in 1562. And this was only the beginning!

With the windmill, a new profession had come into being as well—that of windmiller. It was the heyday of the guilds. Almost without exception each profession or trade was organized in these powerful associations. In the middle of the fourteenth century, Holland's millers met in Amsterdam and founded the "Guild of Saint Victor": the windmillers' union.

Victor was a Christian soldier in the Roman army of 300 A.D. who refused to make an offering on the regimental altar of Jupiter. Today he would be called a conscientious objector. Adding insult to injury, Victor proceeded to smash both the altar and the statue of the great Roman god. His protest was not well timed; it would be another thirty-seven years before Emperor Constantine would embrace Christianity on his deathbed. After having been tortured, Victor was condemned to be crushed between two millstones, but the hand-operated gristmill refused to turn—other versions have it that the stones crumbled—and Victor was finally put to death by sword.

III

Between 1200 and 1300 a series of violent storms changed the map of Holland radically. The sea broke through the dikes and sand dunes in the north and cut a wide, deep path through all obstacles into Flevo Lake. The Zuiderzee (Southern Sea) had been born. Salt water flowed everywhere unchecked and many of the North Holland lakes were now filled with sea water. The tides scoured away more land and the salt killed all that grew within its reach.

"It is quite clear, that because the Frisians are the only people in Christendom who refuse to pay their taxes and firstlings," wrote an abbott in those somber days, "the sea takes away what is withheld from God!"

So back to work they went. Enormous new dikes had to be built around the Zuiderzee and after years of toil the sea was once more locked out of the Lowlands. As a direct result of the sea's breakthrough, a tiny obscure fishing hamlet at the mouth of the Amstel River had become a seaport. A dam with a sluice gate to keep the sea out was constructed, at the same time controlling the river level. When the sluices were closed, the water in the river rose, making it navigable for bigger ships. A dam in the Amstel: Amsteldam. Amsterdam was on its way! Within 300 years she would be the most powerful, and the richest city on earth. Men everywhere would call her the "Queen of Europe."

Many other cities and towns built dams across their rivers for the same reasons as Amsterdam, or because a dike built across a sea inlet would shorten the coastline considerably and eliminate the tides in lake and stream as well. One by one the salt-water inlets were closed. The names on the map of Holland tell the story: Rotterdam, Edam, Volendam, Monnikendam, Alblasserdam, Leerdam, Zaandam, Stellendam . . . or Gorredijk, Nieuwendijk, Honselersdijk, Poeldijk . . . hundreds of them.

"Flee! The water is coming!!" Ever since man lived on the land lower than the sea, this cry has too often been heard. Church bells then tolled their warning incessantly, their urgent voices lost in the howling of the wind. "Save your lives. The dike is gone!" The people fled to high ground, to their roofs, or to the old terpen, if there was time. The sea had broken a dike, widening the breach with every second that passed, pouring inland at high speed, thundering over fields, crops, and cattle, sweeping farm after farm away, foaming through the streets of villages and towns covering all.

Since the year 1000 there have been more than 130 major floods in Holland, and this does not include the countless thousands of smaller ones. One cannot expect to fight a war without losing some battles.

It usually happens like this: a storm born in the Arctic moves south, pushing water into the North Sea from which it cannot escape, since it is bottlenecked by the narrows between Calais and Dover. The North Sea level steadily rises, and the water, whipped by the wind, breaks a dike by sheer pressure, batters it down, or flows over the top. When the latter happens, the water coming over the top digs holes more than 100 feet

Everywhere along sea dikes you will find these telltale pools, some small, others sizable. They indicate that the sea once broke through here. The holes were too deep to fill and were even enlarged by men who needed earth to mend the dike breach.

deep in the soft ground behind the dike, which then collapses into the pre-dug grave.

Everyone knows the story of the small boy who saved Holland by holding his finger in the leaking dike. Everyone, except most Dutchmen. "It couldn't be done," any Hollander will tell you. "It must be a fable because a dike doesn't break like that." They are right—it does not. Yet they built a small monument in Spaarndam to honor that boy. It turned out to be a perfectly sound idea—the tourists love it and Spaarndam is booming!

If this sounds too disappointing, here is what a Dutchman saw in the sixteenth century: "When the top of the dike began to crumble and the

Willemstad's "high-water cannon" was fired to warn the population of impending danger. Church and special alarm bells were also rung to alert the countryside. When high water threatens, a heavy beam is placed in the slot across the road—and every inch counts!—to raise the dike to uniform height.

Old polder farms have outsized attic doors so that livestock can be brought upstairs during floods.

onrushing water had dug a gully that grew bigger fast, I saw a man throw himself bodily into the hole, thus stopping the water until others quickly rushed to help him. In this manner the brave man saved part of the land." It may make you feel better, and maybe there is some truth to the story of the little boy after all.

On the night of December 14, 1287, 50,000 people were drowned when the sea broke through between Stavoren and Eems. This was one of the storms that created the Zuiderzee. Much of the land lost that night was never recovered. Holland's population numbered around 1,000,000 at that time, which means that five per cent of them lost their lives in that single night.

These disasters are usually remembered by the name of the saint on whose day they occurred. There was Saint Elizabeth's Flood of 1421; Saint Felix's Flood of 1530; All Saints' Flood, 1590, when sixty-five villages and 10,000 people perished; 1799 . . . 1809 . . . 1825 . . . 1916. . . .

When a storm subsided, the Dutch quietly took stock of the situation and patiently began to rebuild. First the dikes had to be closed, then the water pumped out. This sometimes took years, and after that it took more years before the ravaged fields bore crops again, for the salt impregnated the fertile soil deeply. Every single tree had to be replaced, every leaf of grass newly sown, for where the sea had reigned, nothing was left alive.

It was, of course, always the sea that did the damage, but the sea was at times greatly aided by man's lack of understanding, faulty engineering, or plain stupidity. Around 1270 the enormous *Hollandsche Waard* (a great polder in South Holland) was created by damming the river Meuse. Now it no longer flowed to the sea, but joined the Rhine through a man-made diversion. This was a most ambitious undertaking, but hydraulically unsound, and some 150 years later the price had to be paid. The inevitable happened: the Elizabeth's Flood of 1421.

The names of the towns of Dubbelmonde and Eemkerke are but a memory today. They were lost without a trace, like ships at sea. That day the sea created a labyrinth of inlets, marshes, and tidal creeks below Dordrecht, where Meuse and Waal meet. In time the *Biesbosch* (reed forest) became a lush wilderness overgrown with reeds and willow trees. Every spring enormous flocks of birds nested safely in the blooming marshes, gaily specked with the bright yellow of buttercups and countless other flowers. Great sections of the *Biesbosch* were reclaimed and turned into polders, but part of it remained the way it had been ever since 1421: a paradise for wild life, and one of the most popular and romantic places to sail a small boat—and to get hopelessly lost. Here, too, the sea will ultimately be defeated, and work on reclaiming most of the water's old conquest is almost finished—much to the chagrin of many Dutchmen who loved this wonderful, silent, wet Garden of Eden.

We all know that people will do strange things for money, but what the Dutch began to do in the early 1400s must be impartially considered the all-time height of shortsightedness. They discovered that the old peat bogs (for this is what the old marshes below the sea had become) were full of salt. If you dug up the peat, let it dry for a while and then burned it, you had a heap of pure salt left. As simple as that—a capital idea! There was only one hitch: the best peat lay on the sea side of the dikes. And now, believe it or not, they began digging greedily in front of their dikes, burning peat, and making money. Wherever this happened (and it occurred most often in Zeeland), the dikes were weakened to the extent that the first storm breached them. Many polders and everything in them were lost, so that Charles V finally issued a decree in 1515 forbidding the practice once and for all. It was about time, too!

Reimerswaal on Zuid Beveland in Zeeland was a prosperous old city. Large for its day, fortified with crenelated walls and solid brick defensive towers. "Built to last till Judgment Day," its burghers must have said. The peat delving damage had been done near here, too, and Saint Felix's Flood of 1530 breached the dikes. The local landlord must have been low on cash, for he did not bother to repair the dikes. Polder after polder was lost and their dikes washed away without a trace until after only a year Reimerswaal stood completely isolated—surrounded by the sea—a strange brick battleship with turrets, run aground in shallow water. Life continued for some years in the city (in 1573 it was plundered by Spanish soldiers, so there must still have been worth-while things in it), but more and more of its burghers left for the mainland. There was no longer any way to earn a living. It seems incredible that the last inhabitants moved to nearby Tholen only in 1634. Reimerswaal became a silent ghost town off the coast. The sea, having won, was in no hurry now and took its time in swallowing up the city. The last ruins were still visible at low tide in the 1700s.

The memory of many of these lost lands is kept alive in legends. Their characters always include fishermen and mermaids, and the motive behind their actions is usually revenge. It is said there was a Zeeland fisherman from Schouwen who caught a mermaid in his nets. Although she implored him to set her free, he refused and took her home. She begged and pleaded, for she had a large family to take care of, but to no avail. The heartless population kept her tied up in a pool for their own amusement. At night she sang a mournful song that no one understood. Her husband, a merman, swore to free his wife and to take revenge. He dug a deep hole in the dike, under the water so it could not be seen. The next storm broke the dike with ease and half the island was lost forever. The merman freed his wife and they were last seen shaking their fists at the few people who had been fortunate enough to save themselves on the crumbling dike.

Still, neglect was by no means always the reason why so much was irretrievably lost. When a dike was breached and had tumbled into the great cavity behind it, the only way to mend that dike was to build a new dike behind the hole. The hole itself was too large and too deep to fill. This new dike was called a ringdike, and it always remained one of the most vulnerable spots. If it broke—as it often did—the process would be repeated, time after time, and in this manner the land would inevitably shrink.

During the Elizabeth's Flood, many people had fled onto a dike near Rotterdam when they saw a wooden cradle ride by on the high waves. In it was a baby girl, and on it stood a dripping cat who, by jumping

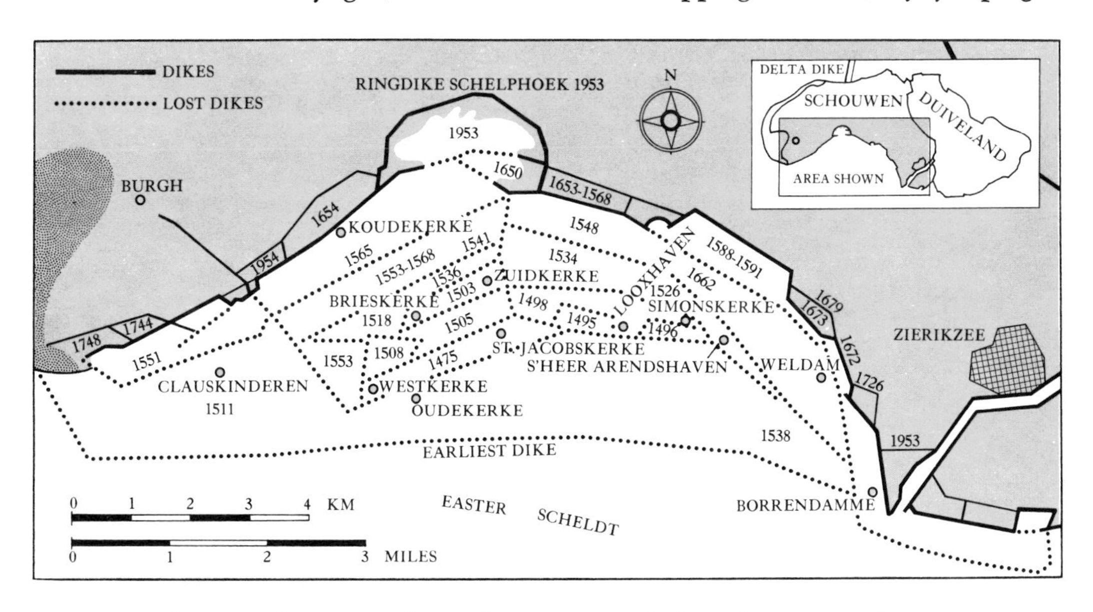

The dates on this map indicate the years in which each area was lost . . . 7250 acres and 12 villages swallowed up by the sea. In 1460 Philip of Burgundy proclaimed that it would henceforth be unlawful for anyone on Schouwen to profit financially from the repairs and upkeep of dikes.

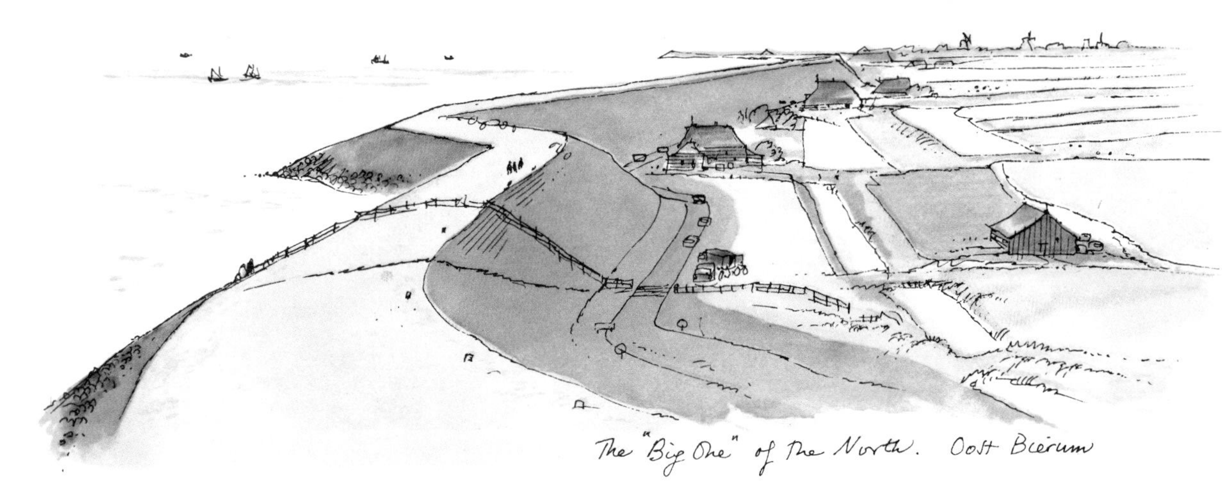

from side to side, balanced it and kept it from overturning. Thanks to the cat, the cradle ran safely ashore nearby, and that dike has been called KINDERDIJK (Child's Dike) ever since. The survivors of that disaster never returned to their low-lying lands, but permanently settled on the dike to become the first generation of the world's most famous professional water fighters. If some day you see a Dutch dredger noisily at work somewhere in the world, look for the home port on the dented, stubby stern. More likely than not, it will be KINDERDIJK, for that is where most Dutch hydraulic engineering firms still come from!

The great flaw in this incredibly elaborate system of dikes and polders was the absence of the central authority that was so desperately needed to co-ordinate and regulate the efforts of a whole nation. It makes one shudder to think that they had to struggle on without it until 1754.

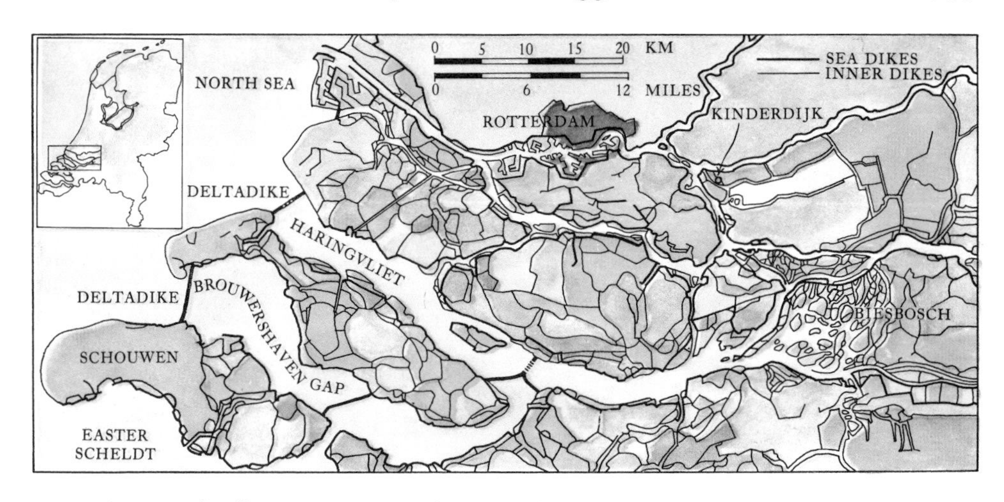

Northern Zeeland's major outer and inner dikes.

IV

Andries Vierlingh was born in 1507 and he grew up to become the first true dike-engineer-scientist that the Netherlands produced. Although he came from a wealthy patrician family (a class whose unofficial motto went something like "to labor is for the stupid"), young Andries did not mind getting mud on his hands or boots. He was always drawn to the dikes, ready to lend a helping hand. He liked them so much, in fact, that they remained the great passion in his life: the dikes, the sea, and the tides.

In 1536 he was an alderman of Breda, a town you must have seen at one time or another in Velázquez' painting *The Surrender of Breda.* A few years later he became the dike count of several important polders, a high position. His great peeve was the lack of understanding shown by his fellow dike officials and their lack of interest in learning more about their jobs. He was probably quite justified when he wrote that his colleagues knew as much about the art of diking as "a sow knows about eating with a spoon!" But whether this was a masterpiece of diplomacy is another question.

Vierlingh was the first Dutchman to acquire great knowledge, based on scientific observations, of the tides and of the sea's behavior in general. He became famous for his skillful engineering and his advice was sought all over Holland. In 1570 he wrote a book on the art of dike-building, but the manuscript was lost. It was fortunately discovered in 1895 and saw its first printing in 1920, 350 years after having been

In times of war the Dutch flooded their country voluntarily, making it almost impossible for the enemy to enter. In the earliest days this was done by cutting the dikes by hand or by opening sluices. Later, turrets filled with gunpowder were built, especially near towns fortified with moats. Now the defenders could wait till the last moment, then light the fuses and swiftly breach the dike, letting the water rush in.

written. This was a long delay, even for the publishing business, but, as the Dutch say, "Better late than never."

The most remarkable thing about this book is that it has lost little of its value today. "Don't force the tides, but guide them," was Vierlingh's dogma, and, had he known the word, he would without doubt have used "streamline." In a letter of hydraulic advice to Prince William of Orange, he urged that "the sea has to be won with sweetness." But he also wrote that "although the Dutch are a peaceful nation, diking against Neptune is like waging war and therefore we must be warlike!" Warlike or not, he died peacefully in 1579.

While the struggle against the sea continued without letup, another struggle had begun in 1568: Holland's War of Independence against Spain. After the empire of the Franks had fallen apart in the ninth century, the Lowlands had been ruled by the Burgundians. In 1515 Charles V, King of Spain, inherited all of the Burgundian possessions, and that is how the Netherlands became the Spanish Netherlands. Forty years later Charles abdicated in favor of his son, Philip II. Under Spain's oppressive rule—excessive taxation and the Inquisition, to name two examples—the country revolted. The seven northern provinces united in

1579 but the fighting was to last until 1648. This was Holland's 80-Year War.

Early in the revolt, two Dutch nobles—the Counts of Egmond and Hoorne—were executed by the Spaniards. Soon the uprising was not only a political but also a religious conflict because the Reformation now spread rapidly into the northern Netherlands. It was not war as we know it today, but an endless succession of widely separated land battles and sieges fought by small armies that were mainly composed of foreign mercenaries. The war often ground to a standstill when one side or the other ran out of money and could no longer pay their troops. These soldiers then either joined the enemy (provided he had the cash), or roamed the countryside, pillaging, burning, and stealing on their own. This was the war on land. At sea the war against Spain was waged vigorously by the *Water Geuzen* (the water beggars), Dutch sailors who had adopted this name after the Spanish had derisively called them *des gueux* (which means beggars in French). Their fleets roamed the coast employing hit-and-run tactics. The Geuzen captured coastal cities, held on for a short time, and then retreated to the open sea.

In times of war, the sea—Holland's arch foe—became her stanchest, ally. When an enemy approached, the Dutch cut their dikes in a hurry, flooding their polders for which they had fought so long and so bitterly. The Dutch then defended themselves behind that belt of flooded land, which was impassable on foot and not deep enough to serve enemy ships.

"We'd rather drown it than lose it!" said the Dutch. Sometimes they

Rusting trophies: captured Spanish anchors hang from Enkhuizen's "Dromedary" tower. In 1573, during the 80-Year War, a Spanish fleet cruised off the city. It was winter and a sudden cold froze the Zuiderzee. The next day all ships were locked motionless in the ice. When the ice was strong enough, Dutch horsemen galloped out and captured the fleet. This must have been the only time in the history of warfare that a fleet at sea was captured by cavalry! Soon another Spanish fleet arrived to clear the Water Geuzen from these vital waters. The battle favored the Dutch, no doubt helped "by the quicklime our lads flung into their eyes as we boarded them!" and the Spanish admiral was taken prisoner.

both drowned and lost it, for large chunks of Holland—voluntarily handed back to the sea—were swept away and lost forever. This was the fate of the land of Saeftinge, when the Geuzen cut its dikes to prevent a Spanish attack on South Beveland in Zeeland.

In 1574 Spanish troops laid siege to the city of Leiden, which contained no Dutch garrison, but was defended by a "home guard" of burghers. The city was ill prepared, for which the inhabitants had only themselves to blame. During the absence of the Spanish, no new provisions had been brought into the city and the population had not even bothered to demolish the enemy fortifications outside their walls. The Spaniards came back and now Leiden was in trouble. (When a Dutchman says *nu is Leiden in last,* now Leiden is in trouble, he means that a really nasty situation has come up.) The besiegers decided not to storm the city, as they had done with Haarlem, but to starve it into submission. The situation became so desperate that some burghers begged Burgomaster Pieter van der Werve to surrender the city. The Spaniards usually massacred the residents of any city which had stoutly resisted them.

As P. C. Hooft, Holland's greatest seventeenth-century historian, tells the story, the burgomaster said: "I, my dear fellow citizens, have sworn an oath, and do trust that the Giver of all good things will enable me to behave with worthy steadfastness. I know that I must die some day, and it is all one to me whether it will be at your hands or at those of the enemy. So, if my death can benefit you in any manner, kill this body, cut it in pieces and hand these out as far as they will go. I am consoled."

This example—and without doubt the invitation to cannibalism—so impressed the petitioners that they left, ashamed and in silence. But it gave them new courage. Early in the siege the troops under Prince William of Orange had cut the dikes to flush the enemy out, but the water did not rise high enough. Now the Meuse dikes were cut as well, and a providential storm pushed the water up to the level needed for a fleet of flat-bottomed boats to come to Leiden's aid. The Spanish commander intercepted a pigeon carrying a message sent by the Dutch relief army, which informed the burgomaster of their plans for the final relief of the city.

On October 3 the Spanish, afraid to be cut off by the rising water, retreated in a great hurry. The population came out of the city and

entered the deserted Spanish fortifications where they found a mixture of beef, potatoes, carrots, and onions still simmering over the fires. The Dutch call this dish *hutspot* (mixed pot; hodgepodge), and it is as traditional on Dutch tables on the third of October as a turkey in the United States on Thanksgiving. The next day the fleet of flat-bottomed craft reached the city over the inundated land, loaded with herring and white bread. Since that day, this, too, has been part of the October 3 menu in Holland.

Prince William of Orange (the Silent) offered the heroic city a choice: freedom of taxation forever, or the founding of a university within its walls. They chose the university, perhaps to the chagrin of some of today's population, because taxes in Holland are very high! In 1575 the school was opened in the convent of Saint Barbara. Soon afterward it moved to the convent of the White Nuns, where it is to this day. A magnificent faculty, including men like Hugo Grotius—humanist, statesman, and a great legal mind—succeeded in making the new university one of the finest in the world within a remarkably short time. Jan Swammerdam, the naturalist, and Hermann Boerhaave, of medical fame, are but two of its numerous eminent alumni. Leiden also produced more than its share of artists, for Rembrandt, Lucas van Leiden, Jan Steen, Jan van Goyen, Gerard Dou, and Gabriel Metsu were all born within the city's walls.

The water had saved Leiden, as it would save cities and country alike, time and time again in the years to come.

V

At the beginning of the fifteenth century there was an urgent need for more land, and it was then that the Dutch first cast longing eyes at the many lakes that dotted the flat, green expanse of North Holland. It had been possible to drain some of the smaller ones with the aid of sluice gates, but with the large ones this was absolutely out of the question. The need for more land was not the only reason for wanting to reclaim these lakes. They often overflowed and during storms their waves clawed hungrily at the surrounding land, dragging acre after acre of irreplaceable pasture to the bottom.

"The Waterwolf devours our land," said the desperate farmers.

As only too often in life, what was good for the goose was *not* always good for the gander: near Edam there was a lake that lay within the lands belonging to the Count of Egmond (an ancestor of whom we have met before). The count wanted to reclaim his lake, which would mean more land to lease to more tenants, a most appealing prospect. However, the people of Edam were less enthusiastic about it in view of the fact that they earned a living catching eel in the lake. So you see how totally opposed their interests were, and this is but one example out of many. The feudal count went ahead anyway and hired workers who closed the lake's connection with the Zuiderzee, the first step toward reclamation. But now eel could no longer enter the lake, and Edam's enraged citizenry, armed to the teeth with shovels, manure rakes, and anything else that they could use to dig with, wasted no time in cutting

the new dike. It was the count's turn to be furious and with some reason, for it was, after all, his lake.

The dike builders returned, this time protected by Egmond's soldiers, and closed the gap. The process was repeated not just once, but four times. Needless to say, the count won in the end and the lake became a polder.

But the problem still exists. Four hundred years later, on March 23, 1961, this item appeared in the Dutch newspapers:

> On Saturday a special meeting was held in Veere's community building, at which the town council bid farewell to all those Zeeland fishermen who used to make Veere their home port. A color movie was shown: "And the Sea Was No More." BY WAY OF PRECAUTION NO MEMBERS OF THE DEPARTMENT OF DIKES OR PERSONNEL WORKING ON THE NEW DIKES WERE INVITED. Veere, as is well known, will cease to be a seaport next month with the closing of Veere inlet, and because of this the fishing fleet will have to vacate. [The capitals in the quote are mine, but that's progress for you!]

Cities, ordered to build a dam that did not suit their interests—no matter how desperately that dam might be needed for the common good—either did what the population of Edam unsuccessfully tried, or

The sea lock at Edam, one of the more than 725 locks in the Netherlands. It was nearby that the Count of Egmond's dike was cut. "I'm kept pretty busy," said the lockkeeper. "Last year 2600 ships passed through." He added apologetically, "Quite a few of those were pleasure craft though." During the 16th and 17th centuries Edam's renowned shipyards lined the canal below the lock. Thousands of India men and most of the legendary admirals Tromp and de Ruyter's ships were built here. Today many pleasure craft are still constructed at Edam.

appealed to the highest power in the land. This might have been the emperor, the king, or the court of the Estates of Holland, but the result in either case was that the work was held up for years at a time.

One day, long ago, a winter storm breached the sea dike near Edam. Along with the water that flowed into the Purmer Lake, a mermaid from the high North was helplessly swept through the broken dike into the lake (so an old North Holland legend goes). When the storm abated, the dike was quickly mended and the mermaid could not return to the open sea. The next morning the milkmaids—rowing across the lake to milk their cows—heard moaning in the reeds. They were curious and rowed over to investigate the strange sound, but found nothing.

The next day, however, they heard the same sound and saw the mermaid follow them from a distance. No friendly gestures, smiles, nor food held out invitingly by the milkmaids could induce the mermaid to come closer. From then on the mermaid followed the girls daily, coming closer every day. One day she had lost all her fear and came alongside the boats, whereupon the milkmaids grabbed her, dragged her into the boat, and rowed back to Edam triumphantly with their unusual catch. The mermaid was widely admired and, after she had been given a bath, the *Dominee* (the minister or preacher) ordered her dressed because "even though this woman of the sea is no Christian, her nakedness should be properly covered." The mermaid turned out to be intelligent: she learned how to sew and knit and spoke Dutch rather well, although with an outlandish accent. (So do I when I speak English, and know how she must have felt about it.)

The town fathers gave her a little house and Edam's mermaid became the pride of the county, drawing visitors from far and wide. The population of Haarlem asked if it was possible to have the mermaid stay with them for a while. Edam at first refused to give up their prime tourist attraction, but later let her go. In Haarlem she was given a beautiful house and provided with servants. She lived there happily for many years, and died very, very old, mourned by her many friends. Her funeral was one of the finest and largest the good city of Haarlem had seen in years and even the burgomaster himself spoke a few fitting words.

Most nations have adopted some sort of animal to grace their crest, or use one to symbolize their national character. It is a varied menagerie: the American eagle, the British lion, the Gallic cock, the Russian bear, and many more. The Dutch—in this case rather unoriginally—have a crowned, fierce-looking lion that clutches a sword and some arrows. Incidentally, he also sticks out his tongue—history does not tell at whom. Looking back, it seems to me that they chose the wrong beast, for the

Dutch coat of arms should really show a crowned herring, caught in a heraldic net imposed on a sea of gold! For the Dutch owe infinitely more to this small fish than they do to the King of Beasts.

The herring is a fish that likes its water salty. Around the year 1200 the Arctic and Baltic seas were no longer briny enough because of the melting polar ice, and enormous schools of herring moved into the North Sea. Suddenly the Lowlands held an incredibly profitable near monopoly—fish. The menu at that time was a boring one, mostly starches. On top of that, the religious calendar consisted of so many fast days and religious holidays on which meat was taboo that this bounty from the sea was more than welcome. Rich catches spelled new prosperity: large fishing fleets were needed and this, in turn, stimulated the founding of the shipbuilding and other industries.

If you were to wake anyone Dutch in the middle of the night—man, woman, or child over the age of seven—and whisper in his ear: "What do you know about herring?" he would, in all likelihood, think you were mad. And yet, chances are better than even that he would recite, "Around the year 1325 herring curing was invented by Willem Beukelszoon from Biervliet in Zeeland," even though still half asleep. This magic formula has been drilled into the people of Holland from their first lesson in Dutch history and they know it as well as a minister knows the Lord's Prayer.

The herring catch was either taken straight home or was put in barrels filled with brine, thereby retarding spoiling somewhat. But this was not good enough. Willem discovered a quick way to remove the herring's insides at sea before putting them into the brine. The perishable fish could now be kept almost indefinitely, and this, in turn, meant that export to distant markets had become possible.

For the first time in history the people of the Lowlands had solid,

cold cash in their fists! The Dutch fleets grew rapidly and their ships rolled home as heavily loaded as when they had left, their holds filled to the bursting point with the many things a country without natural resources needed so desperately: lumber, grains, tools, and cloth. It was like furnishing an empty house.

Dutch ships ventured farther and farther away from home, and the end of the sixteenth century saw the tremendous expansion of their trade all over the globe. Africa, the Mediterranean, the Spice Islands of the fabled Indies. And so the Dutch grew richer and richer by the day. Nothing better illustrates the incredible sudden wealth of the not yet independent Netherlands than the fact that they contributed to the Spanish treasury four times as much revenue as the fabulous gold mines of Mexico and Peru!

This entry for December 1591 in the diary of Arend van Buchell gives us an amusing peek at the North Hollanders of that time: "They have tremendous riches, made in cattle trading and other trades. In the summer they sail to the East and to the West and return with their ships full of riches. In the winter they lock themselves in their houses, constructed out of wood and covered with thatched roofs, because of the marshy ground, but which at the same time sparkle with a remarkable and almost bewildering wealth."

Good Lord, how rich they were! And to think that it had all begun with a lot of fish. . . .

VI

In the year 1542 the small Derger Lake in North Holland had been drained with the aid of pumping windmills, and people began to realize that the solution for reclaiming the big lakes had to be sought in that direction. But exactly how, no one knew.

The man who would show them how—and do it—was born in 1575 in De Rijp, a small farming village on the edge of ever-growing Beemster Lake. Jan Adriaanszoon was his given name, but the world would know him only by his name of honor: Leeghwater (Empty-water). He was a man of many talents: hydraulic engineer, mill builder, and architect. In his younger days he invented a small inexpensive pumping windmill that could be taken apart and then easily and quickly reassembled. These little mills had boards on their wings instead of sails and a tail that kept them always facing the wind. In short, they needed no attention whatever. This was just the thing for the local farmers, and Jan Adriaanszoon built them by the hundreds, put them on his horse-drawn wagon, and sold them all over the North of Holland. And his fame grew.

The "Waterwolf," the scarcity of farmland, and the almost unlimited capital available for investments in a most promising project gave Mynheer Dirck van Oss, one of the "Seventeen Gentlemen" of the immensely wealthy East India Company, a good idea. In 1608 he hired Leeghwater to draw up plans for the reclamation of the Beemster Lake.

Leeghwater's plan was bold, original, and revolutionary. First of all,

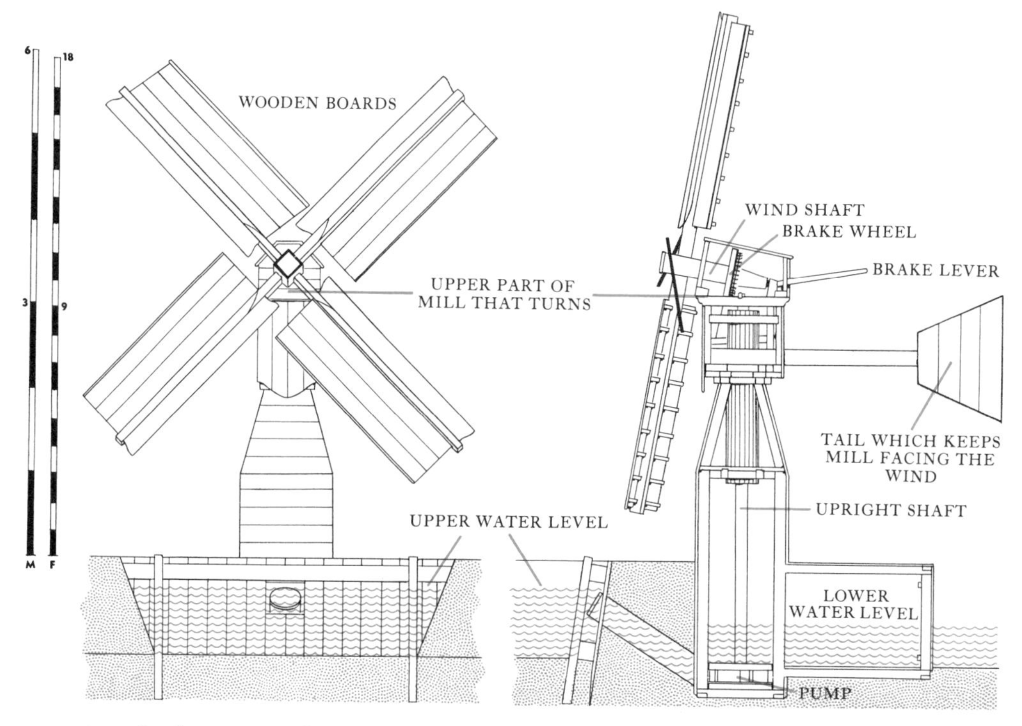

A scale drawing of the small self-serving drainage mill which Leeghwater sold successfully. Countless mills of this type are still in daily use all over the Netherlands.

the lake had to be cut off completely from all connecting waters. Next a dike was to be built around the lake and a second parallel dike a short distance away. These were the two "ringdikes," about fifty miles of them. On these dikes twenty-six large water-pumping windmills were to be built at regular intervals, and these would pump the lake water twenty feet up and dump it between the ringdikes. The mills on the second dike would then pump the water out of the circular canal to a higher level where other windmills and sluice gates would take over till at last the water was cast out into the sea. It is not hard to understand the difficulties of the over-all operation; there had to be a seventeenth-century version of split-second timing. When a canal had been pumped full of water, other mills at a higher level had to take over right away; otherwise, the water would spill over the top of the dikes and wash them away. The windmills were often great distances apart, and an intricate signal system was devised by which they could co-operate closely. Discipline had to be strict: negligence by one sleepy miller might do great damage. One mistake in this complicated bucket brigade could re-flood polders.

The plans were approved, the work began, and in 1610—after many months of pumping—the muddy bottom of the lake could be seen, more of it every day. People waded through the deep mud to catch the eels wriggling in the ooze. Surveyors, too, had begun their work: laying

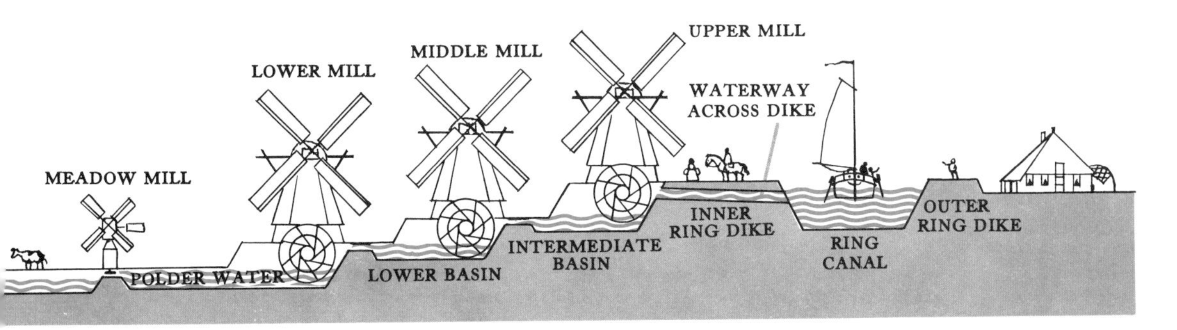

How polder water is lifted in stages. The number of pumping mills required depends on the depth of the polder in relation to the main basin.

out the parcels of land and marking the location of the polder canals. These last served many purposes; all excess water collected in them, cattle drank out of them, and last, but not least, ships that could enter the polder through locks used them for transportation. But that fall disaster struck. A storm broke the Zuiderzee dike and the inrushing water tore enormous holes in the new Beemster ringdikes. Leeghwater and his men fought back for days, but it did no good. The Beemster was full of water again. Some pious souls said: "It served Leeghwater right, for that man should not tamper with God's handiwork. What He intended to be water should remain water." (A strange point of view for any Dutchman, it seems to me.)

The investors were discouraged and some of them considered aban-

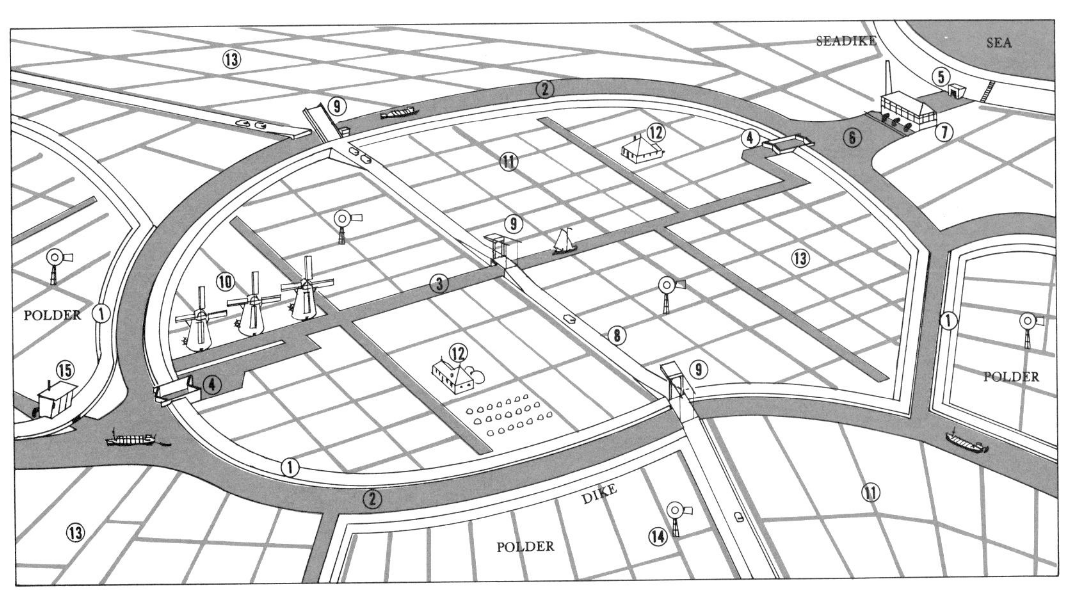

Diagram of reclaimed lake and surrounding areas today. 1. Ringdikes. 2. Ring canal. 3. Main canals for shipping and drainage. 4. Shipping lock. 5. Sluice. 6. Basin (Boezem). 7. Basin pumping station. 8. Mainroad. 9. Drawbridges. 10. Series of drainage mills. 11. Small drainage canals. 12. Farms. 13. Meadows and farmland. 14. Meadow mills. 15. Modern pumping station of next polder.

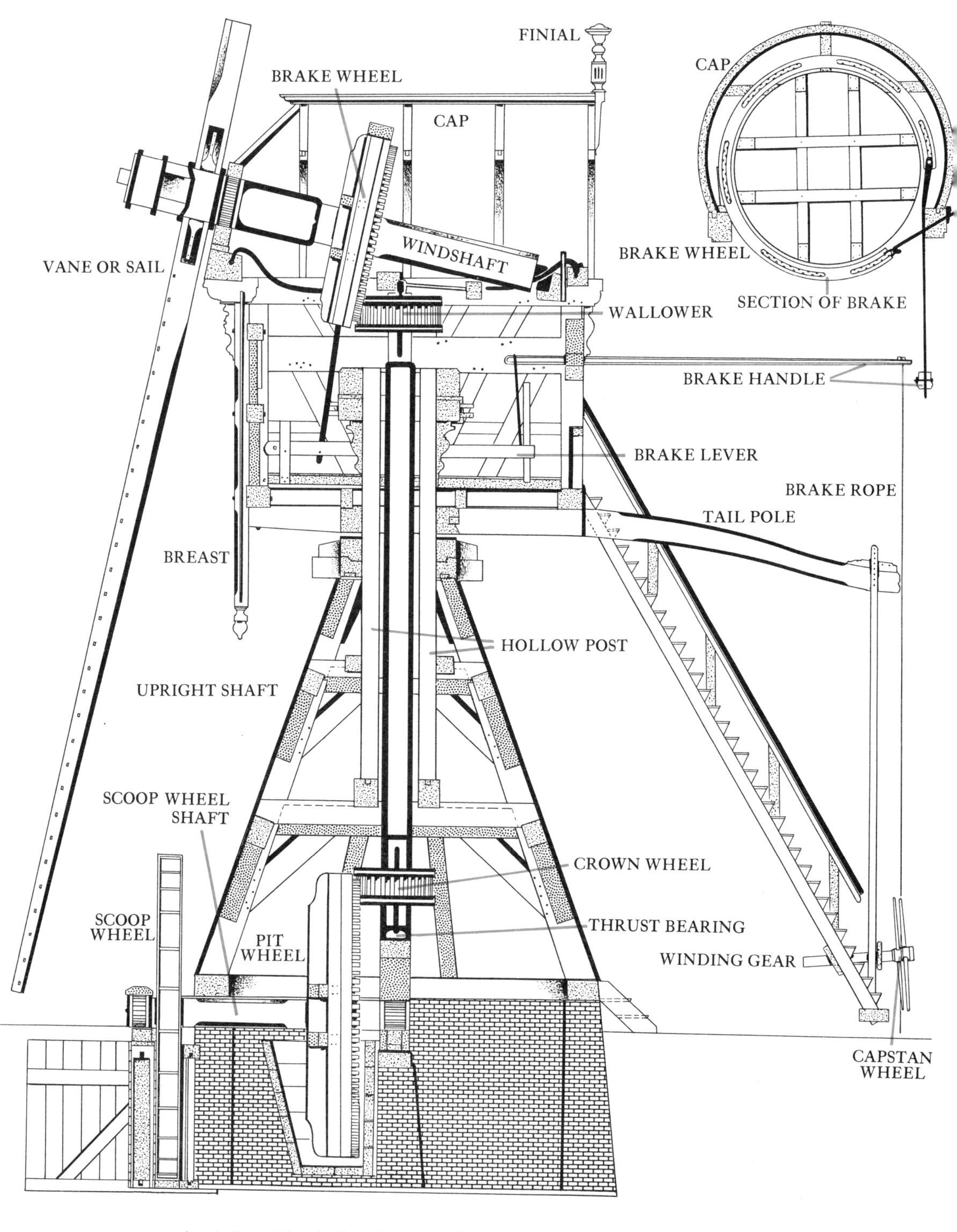

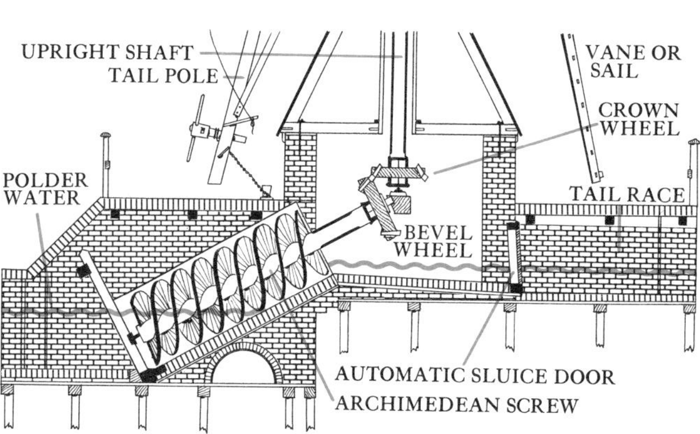

Millwright's drawing of a hollow p mill from the famed Great Comple Mill Book, *published in 1734. Aft 1634 the scoop wheel of old was ge erally replaced by a wooden Arc medean screw (left) which could water more than 20′. Today, when the are worn out they are replaced by scre constructed of steel.*

doning the project altogether. “Let’s not throw good money after bad,” they said. (In Holland wasting money is called “throwing your money into the water.”) Then they thought better of it; the work was resumed and twenty-four mills were added.

“When the Beemster had become dry, in the year 1612, the 4th of July,” wrote Leeghwater in one of his books, “and the roads could be used reasonably well, the Noble Gentlemen Dikers of the Beemster, the Prince Maurits and his brother, Hendrik, and more Great Gentlemen were invited to come into the Beemster to partake of a banquet.” By “Gentlemen Dikers” he meant the investors, and the two princes were the sons of the late William of Orange, who had been murdered in 1584. The fact that they were included shows the national importance of the occasion.

The death of a polder: due to the enormous growth of the population and the need for land for city expansion and industry many old polders are pumped full of sand, burying the lush meadows, canals and ancient farms. Factories and high-rise apartments need a firmer and dryer foundation than the soft polder surface. Here the Buikslotermeer north of Amsterdam is the victim. Rembrandt spent much time sketching the polder country and his second wife, Hendrickje Stoffels, came from Ransdorp, with the blunt tower in the background.

Leeghwater goes on to tell of the reception of the guests in De Rijp by "Jan Sygersz, a fine young man, who had with him a very fine spinster." Prince Maurits graciously gave each of them a gold piece for their trouble. Then the banquet began and the feast lasted all night.

The man whose vision and genius had turned the Beemster's 17,500 acres into land was not considered important enough to join in the celebration. He was there, nevertheless: as a waiter, serving at the table. "I have a large family to take care of," Leeghwater said the next day, "and we can use some extra money."

While the work on the Beemster polder was going on, Leeghwater had also started on its smaller neighbor, the Purmer Lake (8750 acres), and this one was finished in 1622.

The new polders were a great success, and within twenty-eight years the Beemster was one of the most prosperous areas of Holland. In 1640 there were: "fifty estates with lovely mansions and other buildings, 200 farmhouses, 150 homes, and 2,000 people" living within the sloping twin dikes of the old lake, not to mention the fifty windmills that stood silently on guard, pumping when needed.

The Beemster remained one of the sights to see. G. Johnson, Esq., an Englishman, visited there in 1816 and while looking around met a local farmer who invited him to his place for the day. The first member of the family Johnson encountered was the farmer's wife. "You Englishmen are more curious than we are," said this gracious hostess. "I would not think of going to London!" The day turned out to be a great success and was spent exclusively eating huge quantities of very fatten-

Something Leeghwater and the Noble Gentlemen Dikers did not foresee some 360 years ago: French construction crews erecting high-voltage towers and power lines in the Beemster. Anno 1968.

De Eenhoorn, the Unicorn, was built in 1682 and is still one of the most beautiful farms in the Beemster.

ing dishes. Judging by the many courses Johnson describes and by the many glasses of intoxicants his hospitable hosts forced upon him, he never had the time to see much of the glorious Beemster, but staggered belching back to his inn late that evening.

It is a wonderful thing to leave the highway near Monnikendam and drive down into the Purmer. Drive down, I say, for you dip down to the old lake bottom the way you drive down the ramp of a parking garage. It is better yet to hitch a ride on a farmer's wagon (with a fat, squealing pig in the back), drawn by a small, lively horse, and to clippety-clop down the straight brick-faced roads lined by old trees.

Every Tuesday, Purmerend, the old town at the end of Purmer, takes on a look as if a Hollywood company is shooting a movie about Noah nearby. The winding streets are filled with collapsible pens. One street

Raadhuis – De Rijp

houses only pigs (thousands of them), the next one sheep, and so on. The great cobblestoned market place is a sea of black and white cows, mooing unhappily at being tied up instead of grazing in their pastures, and often in pain because they were not milked that morning. Small smoke-filled cafés with sawdust on the bare wooden floors line the square. They are alive with noisy, cigar-smoking farmers wearing their best yellow wooden shoes, doing business over coffee or tall thin-legged glasses of *Jenever,* the famous and potent Dutch gin. (These wooden shoes—or *klompen*—are made of willow wood. They are not a quaint old custom kept alive for the sake of tradition or the tourists, but rather the only practical footwear in this part of the world. They keep your feet completely dry. It is fortunate that they are inexpensive, for a farmer wears out one pair every six weeks.

Outside, horses are taken for a demonstration run. Their yellow teeth and their hoofs are examined by prospective buyers, who then begin the ancient ceremony of slapping hands with the seller while calling out bid and counter bid. All of this takes place against the romantic backdrop of the eighteenth-century town. This healthy, prosperous sight would have warmed the heart of the Count of Egmond, and possibly even those of the angry eel fishermen of Edam.

On the other side of town, a walk of only five minutes, a bridge crosses a busy canal filled with every kind of inland vessel: the ring canal of the Beemster. Across the bridge the road dives into the polder which today, if possible, is even more lush and more prosperous than it was 300 years ago. Some of the original farms still stand—with a new Ford in the barn and a TV antenna on the gabled roof.

On the west side, just outside the Beemster, sits a quiet, sweet seventeenth-century village. It looks exactly the way a Dutch village should look: well-painted farms, a few small clean stores, an old church, a drawbridge, and a miniature Renaissance town hall. On the side of an old house hangs a sign that reports yesterday's traffic problem: DOG CARTS MOVE AT A WALK ONLY!

This is De Rijp, and the lovely old town hall was built by Jan

A "lame" partly dismantled windmill below the sea dike between Hoorn and Enkhuizen. The building behind it houses the pumps that rendered the mill obsolete.

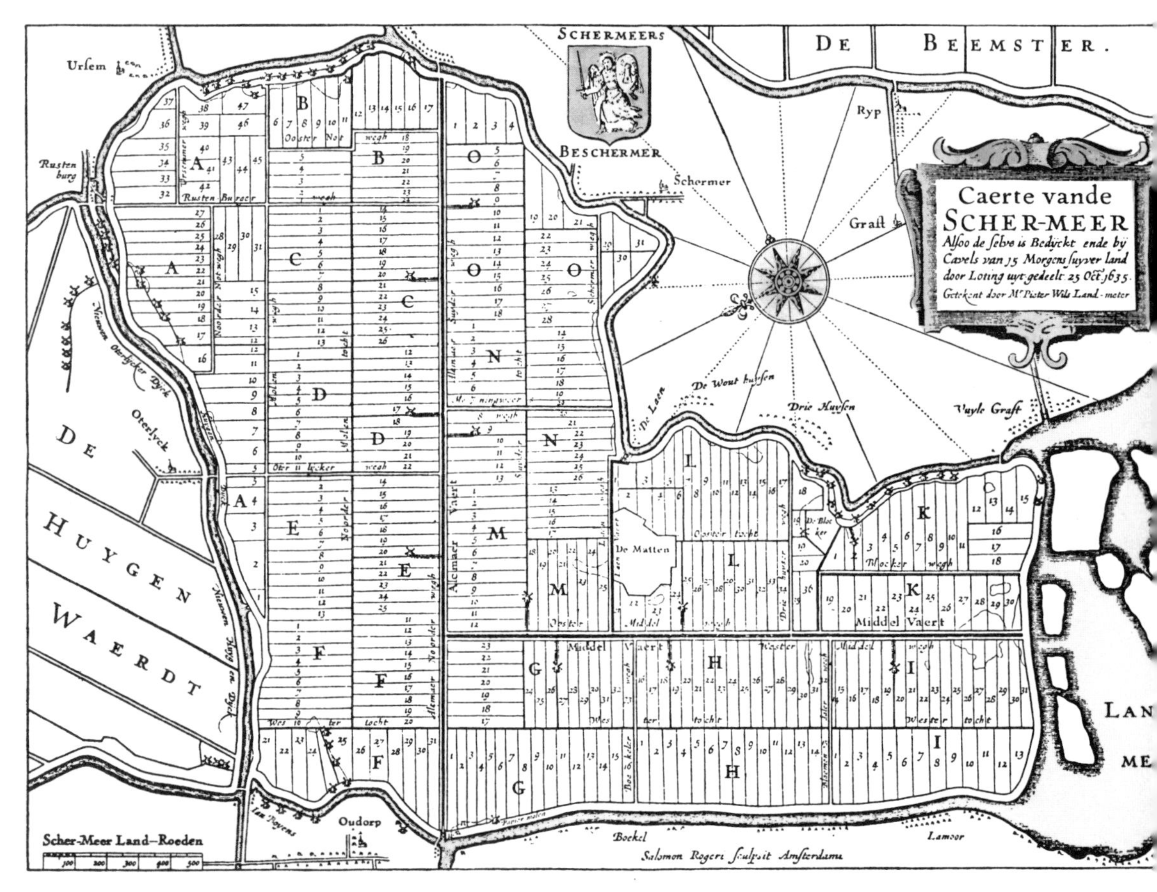

"Map of the Schermer," reads the legend in the cartouche, "thusly diked in and parcelled out by lottery in lots of 15 morgens of pure land. Oct. 25, 1635. Drawn by Mr. Pieter Wils, Surveyor." A morgen was a land measurement that varied in different areas. There were so many interested parties that a lottery was considered the only impartial way to sell the new land. The efficient layout of the polder reminds one of the street-grid of Manhattan. Near the upper right you can find De Rijp and if your eyes are very keen you can count 53 drainage mills on the map.

Adriaanszoon Leeghwater. If you try to find his great windmills on your way home through the Beemster, you will be disappointed. In 1877 a steam-powered pumping station was installed and the old guardians were demolished—all fifty of them.

After the Beemster's successful reclamation the other lakes followed in quick succession: 1625, Heer Hugo Waard; 1626, Wyde Wormer; 1635, Schermer . . . the "Waterwolf" was being licked!

Around 1630 there were thirty lakes in the process of being reclaimed. One of them was near the fortress town of Naarden, close to Amsterdam. Naarden Lake had just been reclaimed when it was re-flooded to help defend the city against a Spanish army. It did not do much good, for the city fell and the population was put to the sword. Naarden Lake was never reclaimed and is a quiet wildlife refuge today.

Altogether twenty-seven lakes were reclaimed by Leeghwater. His fame spread beyond Holland's borders, and he traveled to France, England, Denmark, and Prussia, where he was consulted on how to reclaim more land.

Even though the war against Spain was still in full swing, the economy of the Netherlands boomed. In those days of expansion and prosperity many diking companies were formed and these floated bond issues to finance their projects: the building of new polders or the maintenance of existing ones.

On December 10, 1624, the Lekdijk Bovendams *Waterschap* (water-ship, like a township) offered bonds at two and a half per cent interest to the public. The issue was quickly sold out and they have been paying interest ever since! In 1938 Mr. Albert Andriessen, a Dutch banker living in New York, gave one of these bonds to the governors of the New York Stock Exchange. It is presented for interest every four years to the Waterschap's agent in the Netherlands. The payment in 1952—to pick one year at random—was 150 Dutch guilders, about forty dollars. Here is a last poetic touch: the New York exchange does not keep the interest but donates it to the Benevolence Fund of the Amsterdam Stock Exchange, where the bond was originally sold almost 350 years ago!

The Katwou polder's outwatering sluice near Volendam, built in 1615 and last repaired in 1785! It is through these sluices that water is cast out, or in times of drought let in. In the distance the ex-island Marken, now connected to the main land by a dike, where the houses are built on 12′ posts, well above flood level.

In the triangle between Amsterdam, Haarlem, and Leiden lay the enormous Haarlem Lake, and Leeghwater would not have been Leeghwater if he had not been thinking of tackling that job, too. After a thorough study he wrote his ambitious *Haarlem Lake Book.* In short, he proposed to drain the lake with the help of 160 super windmills. He submitted his book to the government, and we can be sure that it was most seriously considered, for the lake grew steadily in size. And after all Leeghwater was not just anybody. When his plans were finally turned down, the main arguments against it were that the project was too ambitious, that it would take too long, and that it was too expensive (Leeghwater's estimate was 3,000,000 guilders, or about $800,000. By way of comparison, a seaman in the service of the wealthy East India Company earned 120 guilders a year. A few years before, in 1616, Manhattan Island had been bought from the Indians for 60 guilders). And, as always, there was the opposition who wanted the lake kept intact because they feared that the elimination of the lake would endanger the water table, or general water level of Holland's interior.*

In the years that followed, the lake kept on growing in the direction of Amsterdam, and during the next 150 years some fifteen serious plans were submitted to the government. All were rejected "because our experts are of the opinion that windmills are not sufficiently powerful to achieve our purpose." And that was the end of it.

* Any change of this level could have very serious consequences. The whole intricate system of sluices and drainage mills was delicately balanced to existing water-level conditions. A change in the water table through an enormous undertaking such as the Haarlem Lake's reclamation might—it was thought at the time—throw the whole system out of whack, producing either floods or a terrible drought.

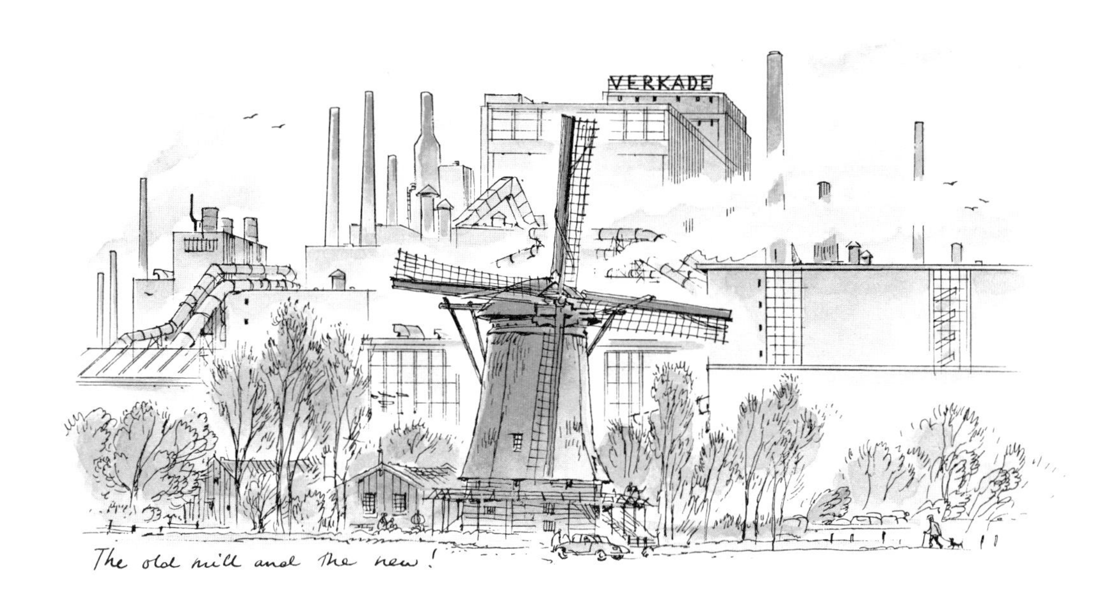

The old mill and the new!

VII

At the beginning of the seventeenth century, Dutch windmill building had reached a high degree of development and, as a result, Holland's industry was thriving. Windmills could not only grind wheat or pump water but also provided cheap mechanical power for all industries. There were wood sawmills, oil mills, gunpowder mills, malt mills, paint mills, paper, glue, mustard, snuff mills, and so on, an endless variety.

In 1594 farmer Cornelis Corneliszoon constructed the first small windmill that could saw wood. Not much later, mighty saw factories appeared in which three huge saw frames moved up and down like the pistons in an engine, driven by an iron crankshaft high in the mill. Many individual saw blades could be fitted within one frame, and their distance from one another could be adjusted. In this manner it was possible to saw thick or thin planks and heavy beams. A tree trunk was laid onto the "sled"—a mechanism that slowly moved past the saw frames. Three trunks could be sawed simultaneously and, with a fair wind, a mill's production could be enormous. Today there are still several wood sawmills in operation.

Long before he reclaimed the Beemster, Leeghwater built an oil mill in his native town of De Rijp. The earliest oil mills crushed only hempseed, from which the oil could then be extracted; the leftover seed was pressed into cattle-feed hempcakes.

Later oil mills were greatly improved and became far more versatile. The oil from coleseed and linseed (for both industrial and human consumption) and rapeseed (oil-lamp fuel) was extracted efficiently by a

Het Pink (the Heiffer), an old oil mill in Koog aan de Zaan, is in perfect working order and belongs to the local windmill preservation society. To the right a few iron-tipped stamps poised above their pots. "That's no teakettle," the miller said to me, shaking his head at my ignorance, when I asked him why he kept it up there in such an impractical place (top right), "it's one of my oil lamps . . ." The diagrams opposite show: edge runner stones in their yoke; the method of driving stamps and rams with a camshaft; the pots where the oil is extracted and the wedges which pressed the oil cakes.

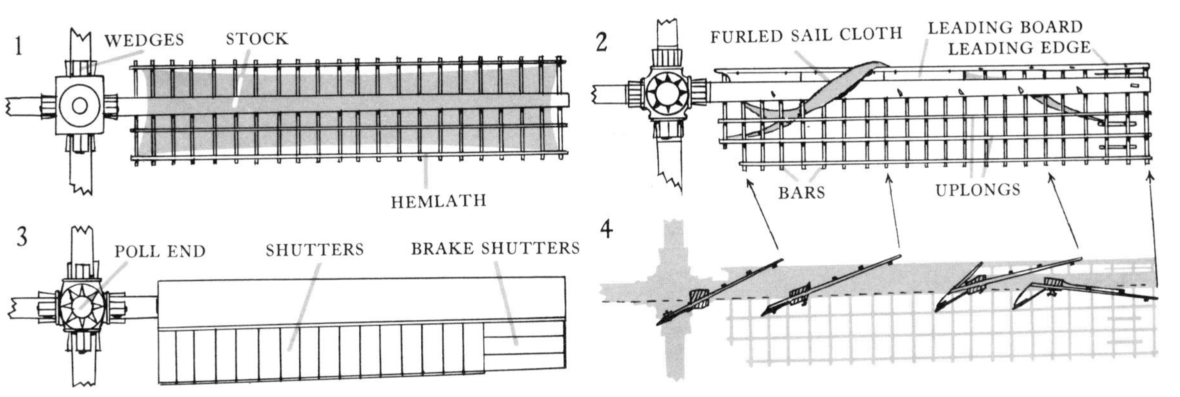

The development of the sail (or vane). 1. Earliest type. 2. Normal type with two leading boards (wind boards) removed. 3. Shuttered type with air brake. This works like a gigantic Venetian blind and needs no sail cloth. 4. Sections of #2 showing the complex aerodynamic shape of the sail.

succession of powerful crushers, rotating twin grindstones that weighed several tons apiece, and by long rows of iron-tipped rams or stamps. Nothing was wasted, for the processed seeds were, as before, used for fodder.

The noise inside the mill was deafening—"miller's deafness" was an occupational hazard—and the ceaseless pounding of the rams and stamps in their iron pots could be heard for miles around. Oil millers commonly worked sixteen hours a day—as did most industrial millers—while the "easy" night shift from 8 P.M. to 4 A.M. was manned by boys and old millers no longer fit for day duty.

The average annual production of an oil mill was 120,000 gallons.

Paint mills ground and crushed colored tropical hardwoods—such as red sandalwood and blue campeche wood—into dust or fine fibers from which dye was extracted. Red and brown ocher, graphite, chalk, and amarillum were also used in paints and dyes. And this was by no means

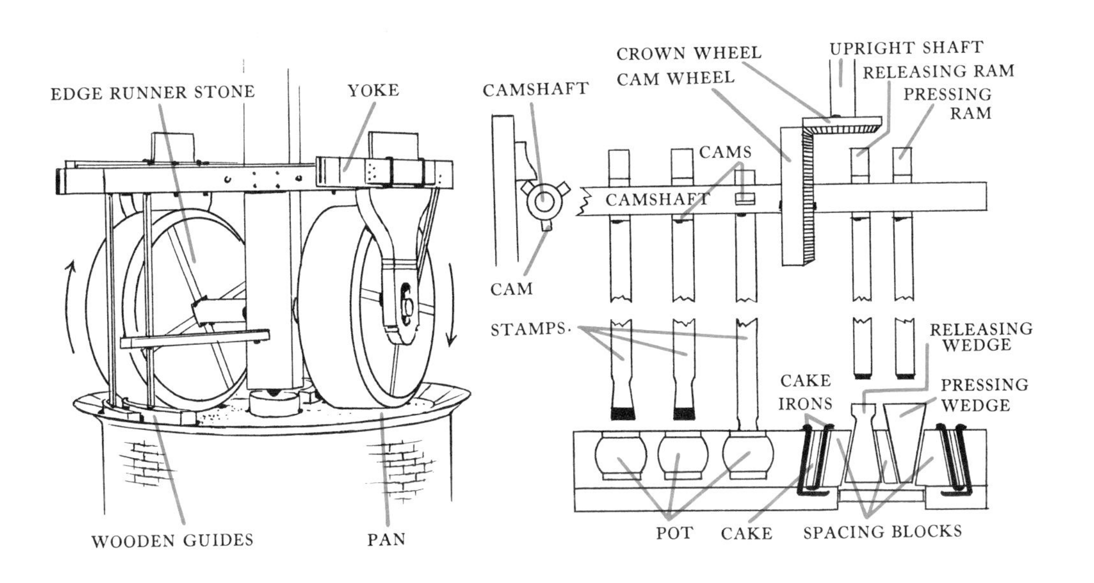

PALTROK SAWMILL

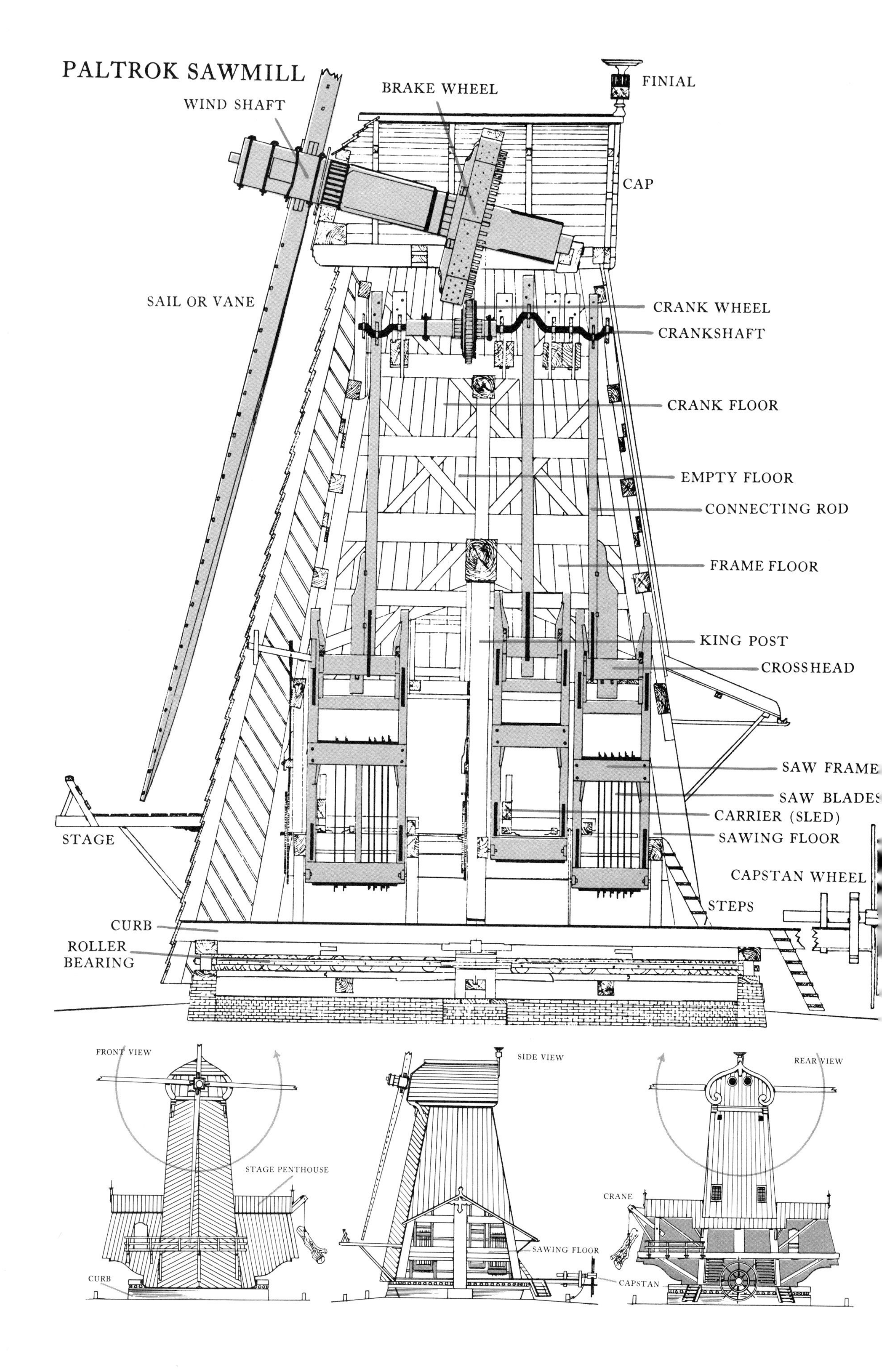

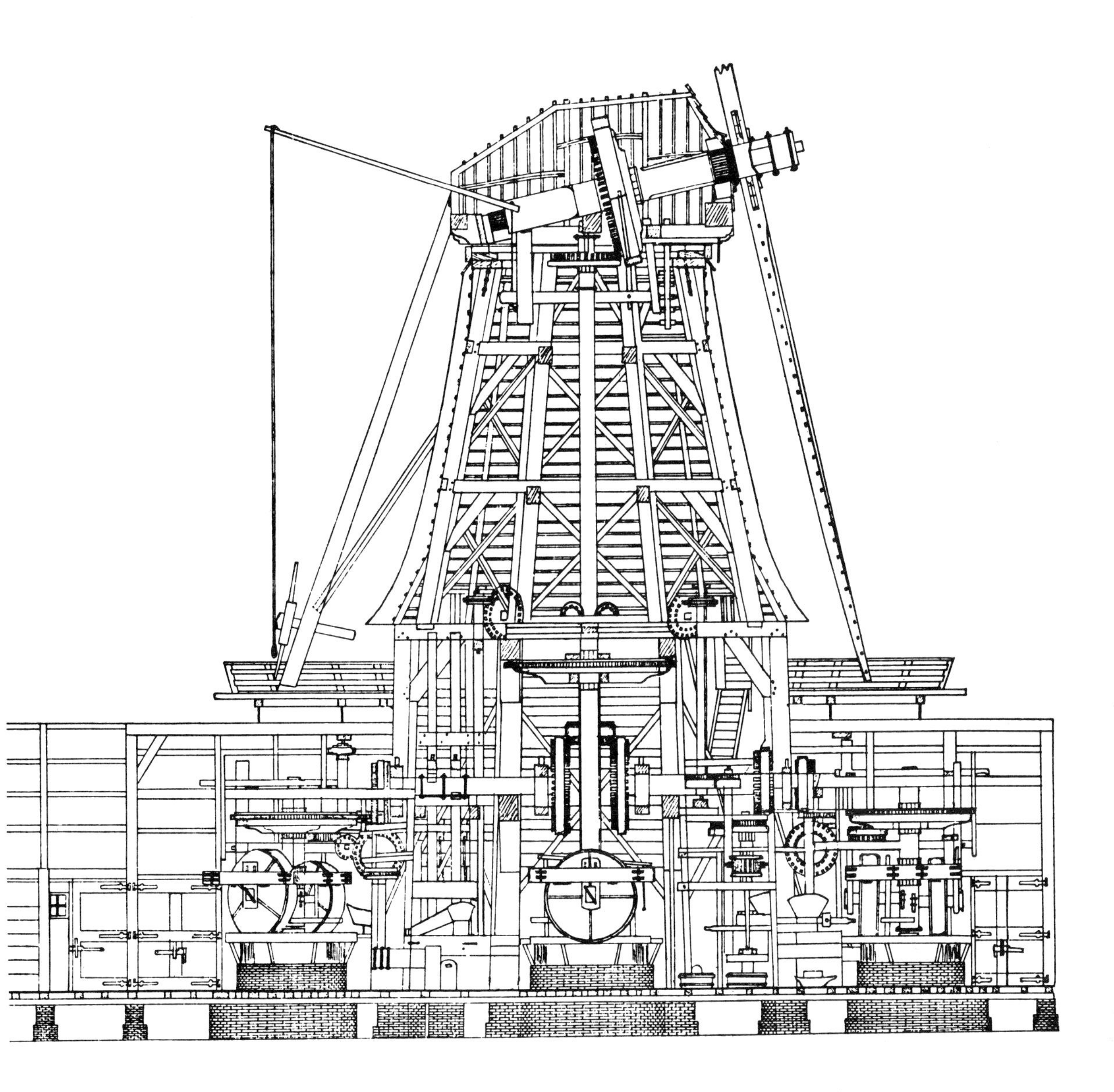

(Above) Construction drawing of De Kat (the Cat), a paint mill. There was so much machinery in a paint mill that it could never be fitted inside the mill body. The windmill was therefore constructed on the roof of the "factory" building. Take a closer look at the lower end of the upright shaft where the crownwheel transfers power to the huge cam wheels of two vertical shafts—just like the differential in an automobile—which in turn drive many other gears and two yokes of edge runners. The upright shaft is directly connected to a very large pair of stones.

(Left) At the time of the Reformation many Protestant refugees from the Rhineland settled in Holland, wearing their traditional black costume called the "Pfaltzrock." Soon the population began to call the skirted, black-tarred sawmill a paltrok. This type of mill commonly has one large saw frame (4′ wide by 6′ high) to cut logs and two smaller ones to cut beams and boards. The crane hoists logs from the water, where they have been cured, to the sawing floor. A large sawmill—and not all were the paltrok type—had a flight of 80 feet. Small ones with a flight of only 25 feet cut the waste from the large mills into strips and slats.

all: paint mills ground poison—arsenic and vitriol—as well as many other pharmaceutical products.

The operation of a paint mill was complicated by the fact that these many different products—not to mention the colors—had to be kept carefully separated. There was the "red room" for ochers and sandalwood; the white "chalk room"; the "poison room"; and so on.

Standard equipment in a paint mill always included a great jug full of milk. This was no mere luxury, for paint millers had to drink huge amounts of milk to avoid being poisoned by the dirt and constant clouds of wood dust they breathed all day long inside the mill.

Paper mills "chewed" up great quantities of rags, in special grind boxes, into paper pulp. Early in the seventeenth century these mills could manufacture only gray or blue paper and cardboard because of the lack of absolutely pure water. At the end of that century it was found that by deep pumping, purer water could be obtained. But even this water had to be further purified in a succession of specially constructed ponds with sandy bottoms, through which the water was filtered and most of the iron removed. Then the water was pumped up into a reservoir high in the mill, where it was filtered through more sand and layers of crushed sea shells. (This shell crushing, incidentally, was done by other specialized mills.) The process was repeated as often as necessary to produce almost mineral-free water, from which white paper could be made.

In the intricate machinery of a white-paper mill no iron was ever used, in order to prevent rust stains on the pure white paper. Bronze or brass was used instead. Cleanliness was of paramount importance, and white-paper mills were always covered with wood instead of the customary thatch, since the latter collected too much dirt and dust.

Paper pulp was shoveled into frames—much as a gold prospector pans for dust in a stream—covered with water-absorbent sheets of felt and then placed in great hand-operated presses. This process was enormously costly

and time-consuming, but it was the only one available until 1865, when an English machine was imported that used the "endless belt" system.

A paper mill with two pulp tubs—and many had four—employed at least twenty-three persons: the head miller, two millers, five women to tear and cut rags, two highly skilled craftsmen who panned the pulp into the frames, two pressers, four movers, two hangers in the drying shed, two paper inspectors who carefully scrutinized each piece of paper before it was shipped, and others who wrapped the paper before it was sent to the customer, sharpened cutting edges of the machinery, kept the mill in repair, and so on. It is curious that these highly trained workers made even less than their underpaid colleagues in the oil mills. In 1870 a white-paper-mill crew of twenty-three shared a princely total of sixty-five guilders (about eighteen dollars) among them each week—and remember those sixteen-hour days!

Glue mills processed cow hides and animal bones from which glue was made. Snuff mills were usually very small, since they only ground the coarse kind of tobacco leaves and stems into powder. Later fine aromatic oils, such as rose oil, were added to improve the otherwise rather primitive snuff.

Volmolens (filling mills) pounded woven woolens with extremely powerful rams and stampers into a felt-like and very durable cloth, which was used extensively until the nineteenth century.

The Dutch called these mills "stink mills" or "skunk mills," and with good reason: Aged urine and rancid butter were added to the mixture from which the cloth was made.

In Holland's South, the body of the mill had often been built of brick and stone, the most readily available materials. Here, too, the land was not as flat as in the polder country and height was of the greatest importance in catching the wind.

In the soggy North, the mills were almost without exception made of wood. In the old mills everything, except their hide of thatch, was made of wood: gears, oak frames, pegs, wings, and water wheel. Since Holland did not grow wood in quantities worth mentioning, it was imported from Scandinavia and floated down the Rhine from Germany. After 1648 wood was imported from as far away as Russia and America. It seems a strange thought that the wood of many a mill still standing in Holland grew in New England.

The fame of Dutch windmill builders spread far and wide and the manufacture and export of windmills grew into a substantial and profitable business as early as the sixteenth century. The inscription on an old gravestone near the Hague reads:

> Here lies Klaas Blom, skipper from Gorkom.
> 't was he who took the first windmill to Spain
> to his own honor and to his country's gain
> in the Year of Our Lord fifteen hundred and forty-nine.
> Died Anno 1615.

The windmills for export were prefabricated in Holland and assembled at their destination by Dutch engineers. With their efficient Dutch mills, manufacturers abroad could produce more than before, and after a while foreign competition, especially from England, began to be keenly felt in the Netherlands. It became such a problem that in 1750 the government passed a law prohibiting the export of windmills. The millwrights now began to export only parts to keep their former deliveries in repair, but this, too, was eventually forbidden. As a result, industry abroad tried to lure the skilled Dutch windmill builders with high wages, but the Dutch government immediately stopped issuing passports to the mill engineers, who were no longer allowed to leave Holland. A millwright who defied this law lost his civil rights.

Still, wherever the Dutch went, windmills soon rose. Around 1640 there stood two wheat mills overlooking the Hudson River in New Amsterdam, and there were also mills across the East River in a small farming village called Breukelen . . . Brooklyn.

In the seventeenth century much of Holland's industry was centered around the Zaan River, close to Amsterdam. Here, in the middle of North Holland's polderland, were the factories of the young republic. And here, too, all the wood was sawed that the great city needed for its phenomenal growth. There were no sawmills in Amsterdam, because the Guild of the Woodsawers insisted on doing their sawing by hand. They quite naturally regarded the wood-sawing windmill as a dangerous competitor that would replace them altogether. Automation and union troubles are nothing new. Builders bought the machine-sawed wood because it was cheaper and the Amsterdam Saw Guild went on strike. In 1631, the city fathers then passed a law that from then on no wood sawed out of town could be used in Amsterdam. The Zaan saw millers now looked for other markets with such success that their industry flourished as never before.

The result was that those of Amsterdam sold even less of their wood and the city passed another law prohibiting Amsterdam ships from carrying wood to and from the Zaan. This time they really cut off their own noses, for now the Zaandam merchants began building their own ships and prospered more than ever. Their fame spread so widely that Czar Peter the Great of Russia came to Zaandam to study mill and shipbuilding. The little house in which he lived can still be seen today.

In 1693 a new law was passed whereby each windmill had to have a name. Looking through the old lists of names is a nostalgic pleasure in itself. Nostalgic, because most of these windmills have long since dis-

Mr. B., owner of the paltrok De Held Jozua in Zaandam said angrily: "The upkeep alone costs me almost a thousand dollars a year and the subsidy doesn't nearly cover that! I've worked him for 50 years (and my father before me) but now I'd burn the whole lot! A national treasure they call him now, mind you! Could have sold him for 75,000 dollars, to a rich American, but they won't even let you do that. Against the law! *I am disgusted."*

The main windmill types in the Netherlands. Over the centuries many different types evolved, each suited to its own task in a specific area. The mills shown on these two pages by no means represent a complete catalogue of the species because there are too many variations to depict here.

1. Post mill, almost extinct. 2. Wip mill or hollow post mill, chiefly used for drainage. 3. Octagonal drainage mill, South Holland type, turning gear outside. 4. Octagonal drainage mill, North Holland type, turning gear inside. 5. Small Frisian "spider-mill." 6. Small meadowmill. 7. Tower or city mill with a stage. Height is essential

to "catch" the wind above the roofs. 8. Corn mill with a stage. The base is built of stone. 9. Stone corn mill on artificial mound. Mound gives height and serves as stage for setting sails. 10. Stone tower mill without a stage. Type used for both corn and drainage mills, called "a ground-sail mill." 11. Frisian "tjasker," the most unsophisticated pumping mill. 12. Smock type industrial mill, hexagon shaped to increase working space inside. 13. Small sawmill or "finger mill." 14. Paltrok sawmill. 15. Modern steel drainage mills; these come in all sizes. 16. Wall mill built on old city walls to attain height.

appeared. THE IRON HOG, THE COW, THE OLD HARE, THE GRAY GOOSE, THE FALCON, THE GREENLAND FISHERY . . . but not all millers were interested in zoology, and the pious ones among them chose resounding Biblical names. However, the population usually gave the mill a nickname that stuck, whereupon the real name was very often forgotten. THE HERO JOSHUA was commonly called FATTY, ABRAHAM'S OFFERING was known to one and all as THE BLIND ASS. THE BETHLEHEM was a rope mill and was called THE ROTTEN TWINE. Then there were the emotionally inclined millers (or their wives) who selected THE HOPE, THE FUTURE, THE NEVER EXPECTED, or FATHER'S BLESSING. Drainage mills had their own wet names: THE SPLASHER, THE SEAL, THE DRINKER, and THE DOLPHIN.

Rembrandt was born in a windmill. Harmens, his father, had a malt mill in Leiden which was named DE RIJN (THE RHINE). That is how the famous painter got his last name: Rembrandt Harmenszoon van Rijn!

Many historic buildings and windmills threatened by the wrecker along the Zaan River are dismantled, then rebuilt and completely restored at Zaanse Schans, which grows steadily. Funds for this unique undertaking are donated by the great industrial concerns of the area. Each weekend volunteers man the mills and—provided there's wind—grind spices, saw wood, stamp oilcakes and grind wheat.

By the time the windmill had come of age, many enduring customs had been adopted and the mill had made itself very much at home in the Dutch language as well. When a Dutchman tells you that "Kees de Jong has gone off his rocker," he'll say that "Kees de Jong has been hit by the mill," or that the poor fellow "is milling." If a man's business is not doing too well, he "cannot keep his mill going." To seize an opportunity is to "pump when the wind blows." "There is the miller and his hired hand!" the Dutch say when a door is blown open. And there are many more.

But the windmill also has a language of its own!

By looking at a windmill you can tell whether there is joy or sorrow in the polder, for by the position of the wing cross the miller can make his feelings known to the whole countryside or convey messages to his neighbors. There was a time, not so long ago, when the whole population could "read" these signals, but radio and the telephone have made them obsolete and soon the language of the windmill will be a forgotten tongue.

The language of the mill is used in everyday work: the wings of a mill placed at an angle of forty-five degrees with all the sails set registers a protest to the polderboard, telling them that the water is fouled by vegetation and that pumping has become impossible. The unfortunate windmill awaiting the wrecker is stopped in the same position, but without the sails. In an active mill this is called "lameness" and indicates "I cannot work because I am under repairs," or simply that the miller is away.

By placing the wings vertically, with all sails set except the one on the lowest wing, the hired hand tells the miller to "come back to the mill on the double!"

During the Reformation, Catholics were being persecuted in the northern provinces and their religious services were banned. Catholic millers then used their mills' vanes to send secret signals as to when and where Mass would be said.

When a baby is born, the wings are set just before the vertical-horizontal position, announcing the happy event. This is called the "coming" position, "coming, for the child that has just come into this world," a miller will tell you. When the wings are placed just past that position,

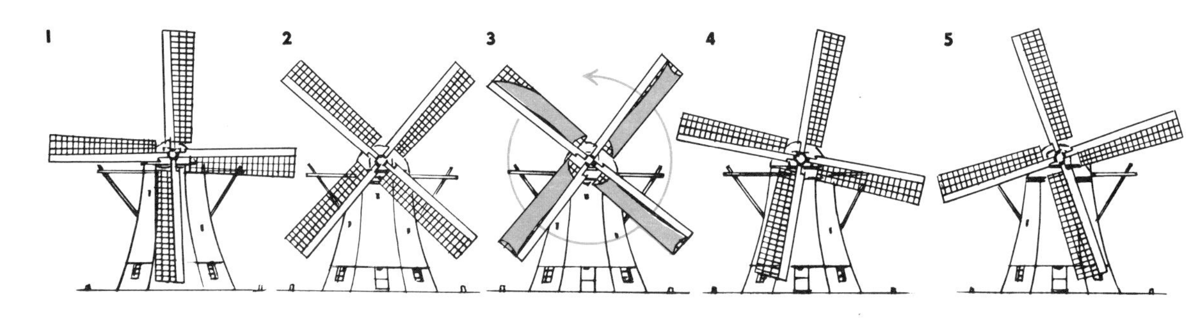

A short windmill dictionary: 1. Rest position for short time during work. Mill stopped here at end of day means "will start work first thing in the morning!" 2. At rest for the weekend or longer period of time. 3. "Come home, wife!" Corner of one sailcloth tucked under; this is an example of signaling with a working mill. 4. Simple joy or birthday. 5. Mourning. 6. Great joy or important celebration. 7. Frisian wed-

it indicates a death in the polder. Then the windmill is in mourning, or "going," because "someone has gone away." The mill then remains in mourning for six weeks—unless there is work to be done—and the wings are turned to face the house where the deceased lived, silently sharing the grief. When the funeral procession is passing the working mill, the miller will apply the brake and stop the flailing wings in a respectful salute until the cortege is out of sight.

The elaborate etiquette of the mill would confuse even an Amy Vanderbilt. The do's and don'ts are taken very seriously and are solemnly observed, but they are not the same everywhere. The many industrial millers along the Zaan River, who considered themselves the nobility of the millers' breed, used to "mourn" even with a working mill. (Aristocracy, I'm sure, had nothing to do with it. A frank miller would have told you that "after all, time is money!") In any case, lengthwise along the mill vanes there are the "wind boards," five on each wing, twenty in all. Of these, sixteen can be taken down. Along the Zaan a strangely mysterious rite was also observed, the origins of which have never been traced. If the mill owner died, all sixteen wind boards were removed—for his wife fifteen were taken down, and for his child thirteen. It was a strange custom, consistently carried all the way down through the whole family. For the parents of the owner, eleven boards; sister or brother, nine boards down. The farther the relation was removed, the less mournful the occasion became. For a dead aunt or uncle, a shabby five boards came off. The list ended with the almost insulting removal of one board for the child of a cousin.

A mill can also be used for trivial matters, for example personal messages that are not necessarily within the law. There was a miller

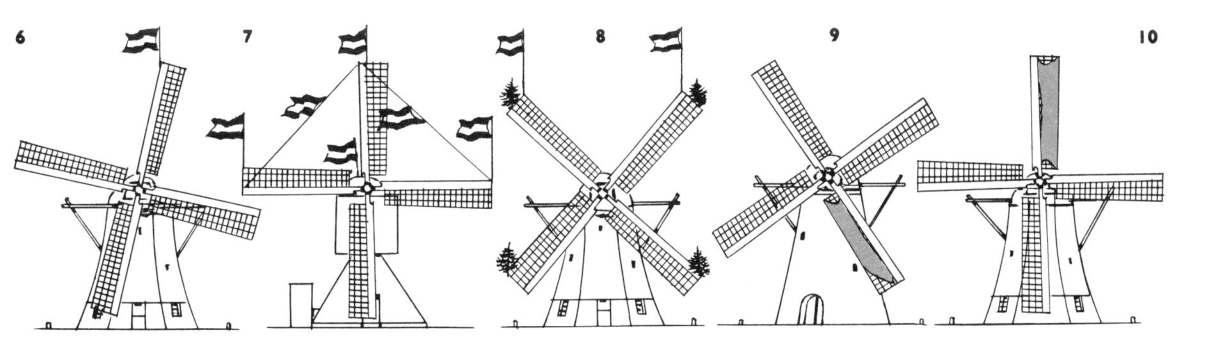

ding. 8. Simple procession position on religious holidays. Evergreens on sailtips. 9. "I cannot grind: am sharpening my stones." 10. "I cannot work: am undergoing minor repairs." There are countless other variations and privately agreed upon signs: the miller's hired hand telling his girl "I will see you after work!" or the miller's wife who ties a dishcloth to a vane, telling her husband to come home from the saloon.

who always warned his poaching pals whenever the game warden came too close for comfort. Rest assured, crime does not pay: they caught the miller. Or a farmer might tell his wife who has gone shopping in the village, "Don't forget to bring me that half pound of pipe tobacco," or "Come home, your mother has just dropped in!" Some farmers still stop their little pasture-drainage mills in a pre-arranged position when a calf has been born and they want the village butcher to come and pick it up.

When an anniversary or wedding is celebrated, the miller goes all out and decorates his mill with flags and streamers. Brightly colored ornaments are strung between the wing tips, garlands festoon the porch, and flashy, gilded stars hang from the latticework. All the other mills in sight do the same and turn their happy, festive faces toward their celebrating neighbor. Between the sails, vanes, and boards, the combinations are practically unlimited and in time the windmill acquired an enviable vocabulary.

"Today the miller's daughter is getting married!" "Mooimaken" (making pretty) on joyous occasions was a specialty of the Zaan area. On working days the decorations were taken down and only a flag flying from the cap hinted at the happy event.

VIII

Holland has 1800 miles of major dikes, but its flank is still protected by the long row of sand dunes—the old glacial ridge. Over the centuries the sea and the wind built up this natural barrier—heaping up more and more sand—but the dunes were only loose hills of dry sand and their position frequently shifted. When the wind created sand drifts, there would suddenly be a weakened spot in this vital barrier. The dunes have lost none of their importance to Holland today: they still bear the brunt of each storm and have to withstand the cruelest punishment.

In 1421—the year of the Elizabeth's Flood—the North Sea broke through the dunes near the small village of Petten, no trace of which was ever found. Now there was a gap, almost three miles wide, in Holland's western "armor." A dike was built and Petten was refounded farther inland. But the harm had been done and in 1745 the sea once more rammed its way through the duneless gap and Petten was swallowed up whole again. In 1796 work on an enormous dike was begun—the Hondsbosse Zeewering (Hondsbosse Sea defense). Nothing explains the vulnerability of this spot better than the fact that not one but three dikes were built here: defense in depth! The first, a mighty basalt-clad giant, always on the alert, is called THE WAKER. A short distance inland is a somewhat smaller dike which constitutes the second line of defense in case the first one should ever fail. This one is called THE DREAMER. Still further inland you'll find THE SLEEPER, the last faithful guardian against the sea.

When Petten was rebuilt for the third time after 1745, no one could

Where the dunes end and the Hondsbosse Zeewering begins (above, looking south). The stone jetties off the beach counteract erosion by the sea. It was here, off Kamperduin (Camperdown), that the last great sea battle between the British and the Dutch was fought in 1797. The Dutch lost. Today they are fighting another battle here and it is one they cannot afford to lose! They are hard at work heightening the

main dike (below, looking north). Huge new breastworks and hundreds of acres of basalt-clad aprons are being constructed. These are designed to break the waves before they reach the main slope. The deep lakes were dug by the sea in 1421 and over the centuries were enlarged by man, needing soil to mend and improve the dike. This is no longer done today: giant trucks bring in mountains of materials.

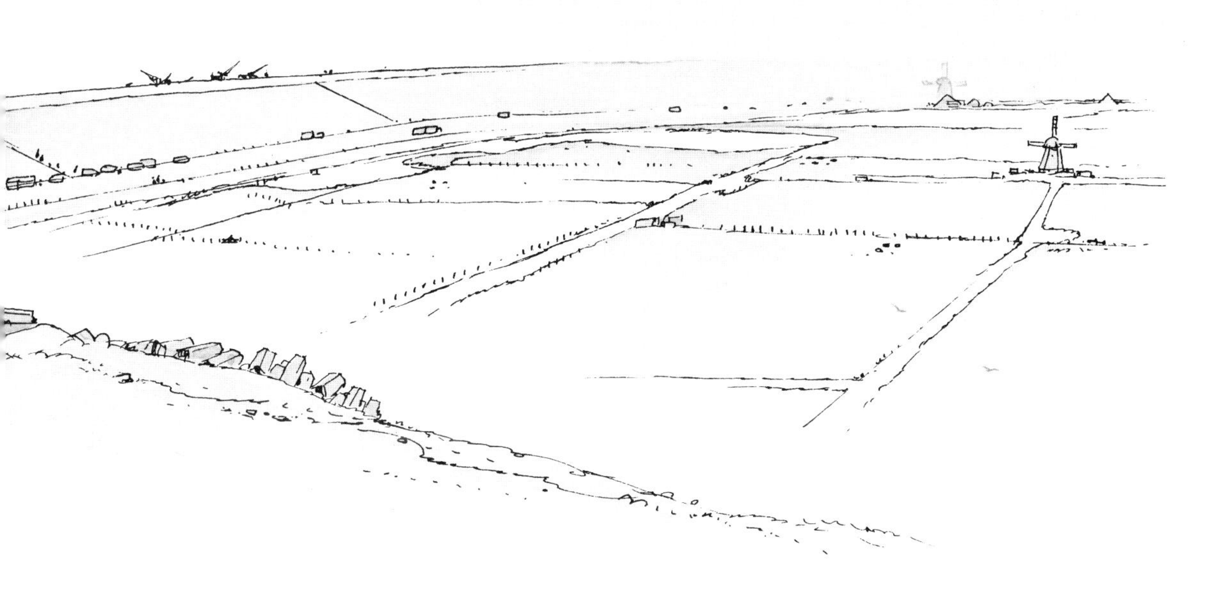

guess that 200 years later it would have to be done again. In 1943 the Germans razed the whole community and in 1947 it was rebuilt for the fourth time. . . .

The shifting of the sand dunes was finally arrested through the planting of a special variety of reed-like dune grass (*Ammophila arenaria*), whose long roots hold the sand together. This dune grass was first planted early in the nineteenth century. Its importance to Holland may be judged by the fact that it is protected by special laws and that pulling it up will bring every policeman in sight running, grimly waving a warrant in one hand and a fountain pen in the other.

Today that strange sandy world exists much as it did twenty centuries ago; a silent world between high hills overgrown with bramble bushes and fragrant heather; a thorny world of wild flowers, thistles, mushrooms, and low gnarled trees, a world teeming with life: hares, rabbits, gentle deer, and not so gentle foxes. And, of course, there are birds of all kinds nesting here every spring. The dunes end abruptly near Den Helder at the very top of North Holland, but continue on the Frisian

Islands: Texel (seventy square miles), Vlieland (nineteen square miles), Terschelling (forty-one square miles), Ameland (twenty-three square miles), Schiermonnikoog (nineteen square miles), and some other very small ones. Originally the dune ridge was unbroken, although Texel was already separated from North Holland early in the eighth century. Even though the government is spending huge sums of money on their conservation, and has for centuries, the islands are slowly disappearing into the sea.

Because of their natural isolation the islands have kept their unique character practically unchanged. There are no traffic problems, and the population raises their famous sheep, some cattle, and some potatoes. Needless to say, they are great seafarers. In 1800, for example, ships en route to Amsterdam had to go by way of the Zuiderzee, and in the village of Den Hoorn there lived more than eighty pilots. The road between Den Hoorn and Den Burg twists like an eel caught on a hook. This is why, as the population of Texel increased, it became necessary to build a road. It was projected to run straight from one village to the next, and this made sense. But some farmers angrily asked, "Why put it across my land and not his?" This made sense, too, and the farmers made such a fuss that an ingenious solution satisfactory to everyone was found. A pig from Den Hoorn was turned loose in Den Burg and it immediately ran home. Notice that I didn't say, ran *straight* home. The road was built along the route the impartial pig took to its sty.

For all I know it may have been a Dutch specialty to make unusual arrangements of this nature. The Caribbean island of St. Maarten is part French and part Dutch. In 1648 the two nations were at odds and both claimed that all of the island was theirs. They were all set to let go with musket and blunderbuss, when some wise soul suggested that there might be a better way to settle the difficulties. Each nation would select their strongest runner and these two would start out from the same spot, in opposite directions, following the coast. A line would then be drawn from the place where they met to the starting point and both nations promised to accept this line as their common border. The Frenchman must have had stronger legs, or have been secretly in training for the occasion, because their part of the island is the largest.

Some wit once said that if you were to draw a straight line through the middle of Holland from north to south you would find only smugglers to the east of that line, and only beachcombers to the west of it.

The Dutch coast is one of the most treacherous in the world for shipping, and the number of ships that have come to grief here staggers the imagination. In the five-year period between 1865 and 1870, 224 ships were wrecked on the coast of Holland! Today, in spite of radar and radio,

it is as dangerous as ever. Stranded ships or vessels in distress are still a common occurrence. The people always risked their lives in order to save the crews, but a wrecked ship with a valuable cargo was nevertheless most welcome. On one of the islands, not too long ago, the minister was preaching his sermon while a storm raged outside: "And so, dear God, if it is Thy divine will that a ship be wrecked today we beseech Thee—let it be here!" Sometimes the islanders helped the Lord just a tiny little bit by tying a lantern to the tail of a cow. A ship's captain, seeing the dancing light in the distance, thought that it was the light of another ship bucking the waves and logically assumed that there was still plenty of deep water between his ship and the lee shore. . . .

On Texel stands an old farm and its unusual name is De Strooppot (the molasses jar). It seems that early in the nineteenth century a prosperous-looking ship was thrown onto the banks nearby. The hull was quickly pounded to bits by the storm and the beach was soon littered with barrels of wine, lumber, and other riches. The population who had been watching this drama with great, and by no means unselfish, interest from the safety of the dunes wasted no time in dragging the treasure home. They had good reason to make haste, for beachcombing was against the law (it still is!), and the sheriff would be there any moment to claim everything the sea washed up.

One farmer saw a promising-looking chest floating in the surf a short way down the beach. He waded into the sea and dragged the chest ashore. It was full of gold pieces and far too heavy to be carried home. He realized that the others would come to share the fun any moment so he stuffed his pockets full of gold and made for home. By the time the chest was discovered the sheriff was around and wanted to know

who had opened it and taken part of the gold. Some envious citizen remembered seeing the farmer near the chest and so told the sheriff. When the farmer had reached home he immediately buried most of his loot. It was dinner time and next to the plate of each of his children he laid a piece of gold. They were eating pancakes and molasses when there was a great banging on the door—the sheriff and his men looking for the missing gold. It was too late to hide the few gold pieces on the table and the desperate farmer threw them into the molasses jar on the table. The house was turned inside out, but the gold was not found. No one thought of looking inside the molasses jar. The farmer kept the money hidden for years until the incident was safely forgotten and the old sheriff was dead. Then he built himself a new farm and gave it an appropriate name.

The most famous wreck off the Texel coast is that of H.M.S. *Lutine,* a British frigate lost during a gale on the night of October 9, 1799. What makes the *Lutine* so interesting is the fact that she carried a treasure: more than 900,000 pounds in gold and silver bullion and in coin. It was during the Napoleonic wars and she was on her way here to pay the British troops on the island. The next port of call was to have been Hamburg, where a financial crisis was in the making. England hoped to avert the crisis by granting a substantial loan to the old Hansa city's bankers. The money on board the *Lutine,* insured by Lloyd's of London, was only partly recovered. The ship's bell was saved and now hangs in Lloyd's London office. It is rung whenever a ship insured by the company is lost at sea. Many attempts to salvage the missing money have been made over the years, and a few bars of gold and a coin were found here and there. But the rest of it still lies off the Texel coast, buried deeply under the shifting sandbars—unless it was buried somewhere else: below an ancient house, or safely tucked away behind the cobwebbed rafters of an old barn. . . .

IX

In 1672 the Netherlands were invaded by the army of Louis XIV. The dikes were promptly cut, and the French were stopped short. The Dutch breathed easier behind their wet fortress, but when winter arrived, the "moat" froze. The French armies now advanced over the ice and had almost captured Amsterdam when a providential sudden thaw melted the ice, forcing the French to withdraw immediately in great disorder.

In 1730 Holland was invaded again. This time the Dutch did not flood their country to keep the enemy out because the enemy was everywhere already, a fifth column that had begun to infiltrate Holland quietly years before. The invader was not an army with pikemen and cannon, but a bivalved shell animal, the pile worm, that had a voracious capacity for wood. The *Limnoria*'s business end was its rasp-like mouth, only a quarter inch long, although the soft, worm-like body could reach a length of one foot. The attack had come quite suddenly, and the pile worm's tremendous appetite made short work of the wooden sea defenses. Two weeks after its birth a *Limnoria* found himself a piece of wood and waited until its teeth had sufficiently developed. Then the worm made itself at home inside the wood and spent the rest of its life boring through the wood.

Enormous quantities of wood had been used in Holland's defense: dikes were protected by row upon row of poles to break the water's force. Wooden poles anchored the reed casings of the reed dikes; sluice gates and locks were made of wood. The edgings along the canals in the

Although wood is no longer used in the basic construction of dikes, you can see sturdy posts and pilings embedded everywhere in the basalt aprons of sea dikes, standing in straight rows, like soldiers on parade. Their life is short, however, and a small army of men is constantly at work to replace rotted and broken pilings.

An old, but still efficient pole screen on Wieringen Island (below). New ones are now made with prefabricated concrete sections that require no upkeep at all.

cities were wooden, as were the foundations of all bridges. But there was more. Beginning in 1440 a new type of dike had been introduced—the pole dike. These consisted of a solid vertical wall of heavy wooden beams, driven into the ground so close together that the water could not pass through.

The consternation in Holland cannot be imagined; people talked of little else, but a defense against the menace seemed impossible. The press abroad predicted that Holland was doomed to disappear, that "within a year the Netherlands will have been drowned by the North Sea." And at first it seemed very likely at that. Churches were crowded with fearful people, fervently praying to be delivered from this "scourge of God." The most amazing stories appeared in foreign newspapers, one of which was that "this worm has a head so strong that even hammer blows cannot kill it!"

Now this was, of course, nonsense, but for a while the danger was grave indeed. Since it looked as if the pile worm had come to stay, no more wood was used in new construction and all existing wood in the old structures was replaced by stone. Stones were also placed on the outside of the dikes—at great expense—and after a few years everyone agreed that the pile-worm invasion had been a blessing in disguise.

In 1754, 333 years after the Elizabeth's Flood, the states of Holland and West Friesland made a momentous decision; they appointed a Director General of the Nation's River and Sea Works to supervise and co-ordinate the fight against the water. It was about time, too! Christian

Hoogendijks' pumping station just outside Rotterdam. Drawn after a 1787 print.

Brunings held the job for thirty-five years, and his accomplishments in bringing order where chaos had reigned can never be sufficiently praised. After he stepped down, the title of his office was changed and his successor became the Director of *Waterstaat* (the State of the Water).

Steven Hoogendijk from Rotterdam was a wealthy manufacturer who had a hobby: he liked to tinker. Most tinkerers make napkin rings or hammer ugly ashtrays out of copper. Not so Mynheer Hoogendijk; in 1784 Hoogendijk built himself a steam engine. This was an ambitious project because the steam engine had been invented by James Watt only fifteen years before. When Hoogendijk had finished his machine he quite naturally asked himself "What am I going to do with it now?" Then he had an inspiration and attached a homemade water pump to his machine. This was fun. The steam engine was noisy, fire leaped out of its skinny stack, and billowing clouds of steam and black smoke rose into the sky. It worked after a fashion, but Hoogendijk was disappointed—his machine could do less than half the work of a drainage windmill. The best steam engines were built in England and so in 1787 he ordered one from there, and an iron pump to go with it as well. No sooner was this new fire machine installed in the Blijdorp polder than it was found that it could outpump two windmills with ease. Now he was on the right track!

When the first windmills had been installed, more than 500 years before, the farmers had bitterly complained that the turning wings would "scare the birds away, so we cannot find any more of those delicious eggs in our fields." There is a Dutch saying: "What a farmer doesn't know he doesn't like." Well, they lived up to this again and asked the local magistrate to ban the engine. "That fire machine, it'll set the whole neighborhood on fire, as sure as we stand here!" they said. When this argument proved ineffective, the farmers assured everyone willing to listen that their cows were becoming so nervous and upset that milk production had already dropped disastrously. This was, of course, a patent lie. Yet the machine was stopped.

Then in the fall of 1787 there was a lot of rain and not enough wind to operate the windmills. The level in the Blijdorp polder rose and finally a delegation of red-faced farmers asked if it would by any chance be possible to "turn that fire machine on." They quickly added, "For free, of course!" Soon smoke billowed once more and within an amazingly short time the water level in the polder was brought under control. And that of the next polder as well!

In view of the pumping steam engine's remarkable success, it seems inexplicable that the machine was forgotten for the next twenty years. The beginning of the nineteenth century saw their revival in Holland and in 1804—eleven years before Waterloo—there were three permanent steam-driven pumping stations. This time they were here to stay.

When the people from Leiden got up on November 30, 1836, and pushed their bedrooms curtains aside, they were in for the surprise of their lives. During the stormy night the water of the Haarlem Lake had inundated the city, which now resembled an ice-cold Venice. Twenty-three miles to the northwest, the burghers living on the outskirts of Amsterdam had the same unexpected experience.

In the sixteenth century there had been a group of small lakes here; in time they were united by the old "Waterwolf." The population had speeded up the creation of the big lake by digging for peat, the com-

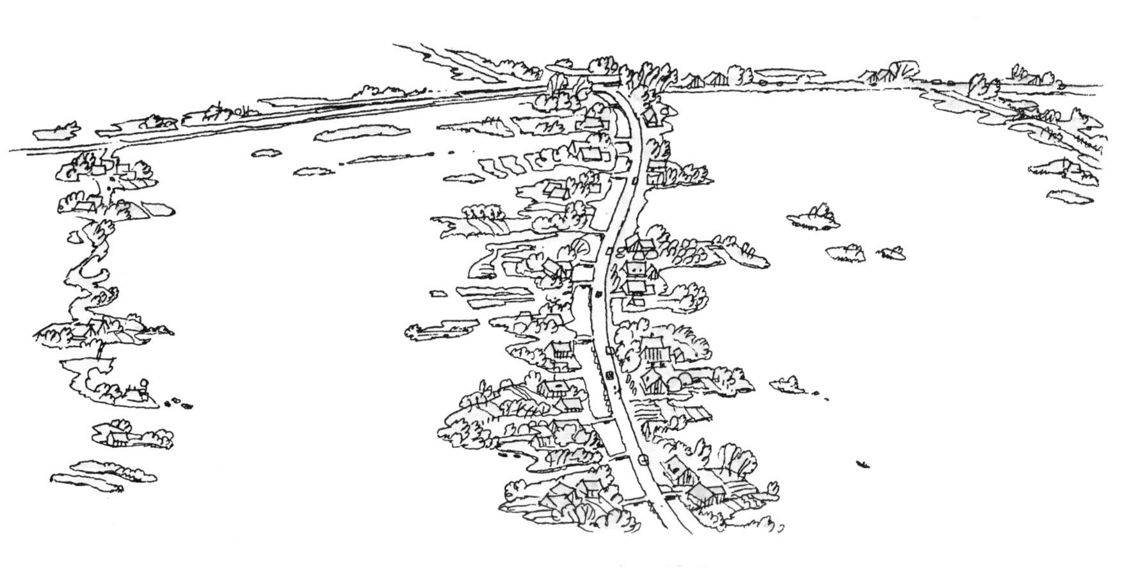

The Dutch have always made more land but after digging century after century for peat only the tiny plots the diggers lived on were left untouched. All that now remains is the skeleton of the land, as in the Reeuwijk Lakes.

mon fuel for Dutch stoves. In 1531 the lake measured 14,000 acres. In 1547 it had increased to 36,000 acres, and in 1740 these had grown to 41,000 acres. On that cold morning in 1836 there were some 45,500 acres of Haarlem Lake. In 300 years 30,500 acres had been devoured by the lake, not to mention the villages of Vijfhuizen, Rijk, and Nieuwerkerk, of which not a trace remained. This was a game the Dutch could ill afford. The problem was by no means a new one: ever since Leeghwater's unrealized dream, others had been submitting plans to turn the lake into land . . . 1659, 1737, 1742, 1743, 1808. . . .

In 1795 French revolutionary troops had occupied the Netherlands and founded the "Batavian Republic," misusing the name of the old tribes. Eleven years later the republic became a kingdom when Napoleon —that champion nepotist—crowned his brother King of Holland. The remarkable thing was that Louis Napoleon took Dutch interests so much to heart that he turned out to be rather a popular monarch. When his brother wanted to make Holland an integrated part of France, Louis Napoleon quit indignantly. The Dutch were sorry to see him go.

After the Battle of Waterloo in 1815 the old republic of the United Netherlands was not revived; instead, Holland became a kingdom. In 1819 King Willem I, the "Merchant King," gave his royal permission to create a new plan for reclaiming the Haarlem Lake. At the same time the Haarlem "Society of Sciences" offered a prize for the best of them. Several excellent propositions were sent in, but with no results whatsoever.

It took the violent storm of 1836 to get things moving again. By royal decree a commission was set up which promptly presented its recommendations along with a complete set of plans to the lower house of the government. At this point you know the Dutch well enough to guess that things were not that simple. It was "the Count of Egmond versus Edam" all over again.

A detail that was missing in Leeghwater's plans, as it was in all the others. The Amsterdam–Rotterdam highway (Europe 10) passing under the Haarlem Lake ring canal, Holland's only aqueduct.

The city of Leiden made a lot of money issuing fishing licenses for the lake, which, by the way, was the only place in Holland where catfish up to 150 pounds were caught. The people of Haarlem were unhappy about the project because they disposed of their sewage in the lake. The Rijnland Waterschap was worried about the water level in their fief, for they dumped their surplus water into Haarlem Lake. But after negotiating and arguing for two years, the House approved the plans, and in 1839 a loan issue to finance the work was opened for subscription.

The plan differed not too much from Leeghwater's, but, instead of his 160 windmills, steam would do the job. In 1840 work on the twin dikes was begun, and in 1849 the first of "three gigantic steam pumps of tremendous strength; yes, of almost four hundred horsepower each!" pumped the first water out of the lake. (The turbines of the *Queen Mary* generated 160,000 h.p.!) This time Leeghwater was not forgotten: one of the old pumping stations still bears his name.

After three years and three months of continuous pumping, the lake fell dry on the first of July, 1852, three days short of the 240th anniversary of the same event in Beemster. The total bill came to 9,000,000 guilders, but the sale of the land eventually brought almost 8,000,000 guilders. The government was a million out of pocket, but had one big headache less: the Haarlem Lake would never overflow again. And it seems cheap at that.

Now the building of roads and canals was begun. Until then reclamations had been the result of private enterprise and the Dutch government had no experience whatever in the social aspects connected with the actual settling of the new land. Roads, drinking water, and sewage-disposal facilities were not available when the first people arrived. Yet, like their ancestors who hesitantly moved into the soggy marshlands so long ago, people straggled into the muddy vastness of the new polder. For the first years they were beset by poverty, hunger, and disease.

Cruquius' Engine Room –

"Leeghwater," the first pumping station, was put into operation in 1845. The "Lijnden" followed in 1848, the "Cruquius" in 1849. All three were named for visionary planners of the lakes' reclamation. The first two, modernized in 1932 and 1954, keep the old lake dry with their diesel pumps. "Cruquius" was de-commissioned in 1933 and is now a museum, its engine bright as ever, although swallows nest high up in the machinery. The 350-h.p. engine moved nine great cast-iron levers, each connected to a pump outside.

But they stuck it out, digging, planting, and building. Two years after man's arrival, a first harvest of oats and rapeseed was gathered. The old Haarlem Lake was made a separate municipality, and when the first local election was held in 1855, all sixty eligible voters proudly showed up at the polls!

Today the area is one of the most prosperous in the nation and, because of the continued lowering of the water table in the polder, the land produces more than ever. A great variety of crops is grown, and now the flower-bulb industry has moved in. Chances are that some of the hyacinths, crocuses, or daffodils in your garden were "born" here.

In a corner of Haarlem Lake, near Amsterdam, there was a small harbor where ships found refuge during storms. It was called Schiphol—"ship hollow." Few people realize when they arrive at Schiphol, Amsterdam's great international airport, where giant jets roar down runways far below sea level, that they are standing on the bottom of the old Haarlem Lake. It is stranger still to think that some eighteen feet above these runways a sea battle was fought during the Eighty-Year War.

The "Scratcher" at work —

X

Early in the nineteenth century, Amsterdam, the "Queen of Europe," fell on bad days because a sandbar blocked the entrance to her harbor. This had not happened overnight. Ships had steadily grown in size and now drew so much water that the port had become inaccessible. For some time ships were lifted across the sandbar by "ships' camels." These were two large pontoons that were placed along each side of the vessel. When their valves were opened, the pontoons sank. Then they were firmly attached to the ship and the water was pumped out of them. As they rose, the ship rose with them and could be towed into port. But this was a time-consuming nuisance, and Amsterdam was no longer a seaport of note.

Between 1819 and 1824 a canal was dug over the full length of North Holland. It had locks at both ends and reached the sea near Den Helder. It was quite a canal: some twenty-eight feet deep and 140 feet wide. Amsterdam was now an inland port about forty-five miles from the open sea. But ships grew bigger and bigger and in 1870 the Dutch did something drastic. They dug a canal straight to the North Sea and cut the dunes at IJmuiden. Amsterdam was saved as a seaport and ships enter every day through the world's largest locks.

The North Sea Canal has to be constantly dredged to maintain the proper depth, but this is nothing new to the Dutch; they have been at that for some 500 years. The silting in of their harbors has always been a problem. Before the invention of the bucket dredge, Amsterdam's

A clunking and creaking dredge hungrily eats its way into the bank, widening the North Sea Canal. The soil—a precious commodity in the Netherlands—is put in barges and used elsewhere to strengthen the canal's dikes and as fill for polders being prepared for industry. In a small work harbor the sinker pieces are built that will reinforce the new shores, keep the soil in place and protect them from the wash of passing ships. "The five of us started this one at eight this morning," said the foreman at 10 A.M., standing up to his hips in the water. "In an hour he'll be sunk. Oh, it's only a little one . . . you should have seen the ones we built in the Zuiderzee! Even so, it'll take thirty tons of stone to get 'em down. Yes mijnheer, he's nicely put together, you could sail on him to England if you had to! Shame you were not here yesterday. The dredge suddenly stopped and they yelled to us that they had an elephant in a bucket. And sure enough, they had a skull with two long tusks. The mijnheer from the University said it was a 'masterdont' or some name like that."

harbor was plied by a clumsy wooden barge from which great wooden rakes hung suspended. The rakes scratched the bottom, stirring up sand and mud particles which the outgoing tide then carried to sea. With this primitive tool the Dutch kept their harbors and canals open; that "scratcher" must have been an effective piece of equipment since it was in use till well into the 1800s.

In the sixteenth century, the "Amsterdam mudmill" was invented. This was the great-granddaddy of all dredgers in the world. Four men on huge treadwheels provided the power, and the dredged-up mud was dumped into barges and used to make new land. The four human mice must have gotten tired, gone on strike, or just plain quit, because soon a brand-new five-horsepower model was introduced. This bigger craft had living quarters for the crew and a stable for five horses! "Noah's Ark" was so successful that most European ports with similar problems ordered them and kept them in daily use until 1860. Planned obsolescence is obviously a very recent invention.

Rotterdam suffered from the same ailment that almost choked off Amsterdam's commerce, and it was saved in the same manner. Here, too,

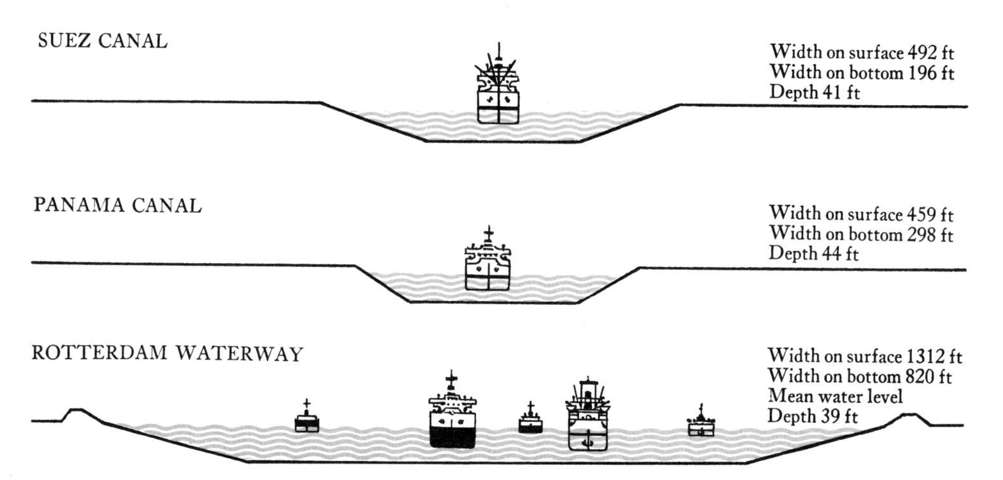

Little Holland has had to build some very big things!

". . . and do everything which is decent and right . . . then heighten and strengthen the dikes!" After 2000 years they are still at it: raising the crown of the dike protecting northern Friesland 12 feet. Far offshore, suction dredges move enormous quantities of sand from the sea bottom to the dike through steel pipes which float on pontoons. When the distance is too great to move the slush, booster pumping stations provide the additional push.

an enormous canal was dug to the sea, straight through the dunes, and again the unorthodox gamble paid off. Today Rotterdam is the world's busiest port, serving some 30,000 ships a year!

Over twenty per cent of Holland is below sea level, and more than sixty per cent of the population lives in this portion of the country. Through the ages the sea stole 1,400,000 acres away, but the Dutch took 1,800,000 acres back. So the score is more than even.

It is most unfortunate, but the Dutch cannot sit back and relax—not now, nor ever. For one thing, Holland is slowly sinking, and the level of the sea is steadily rising, a most uncomfortable combination. When—and if—the polar ice caps and the Scandinavian glaciers melt, the oceans of the world will rise some 150 feet. And Holland's highest dikes are only twenty feet above high water. These Scandinavian and Alpine glaciers actually have been melting rapidly during the past 100 years. Scandinavia, being relieved of this fantastic burden of ice, has been rising. Holland, on the other side of an invisible seesaw in the earth's crust, has been sinking at the same rate. For this reason alone, Holland's dikes have

Friesland – On top of the dike –

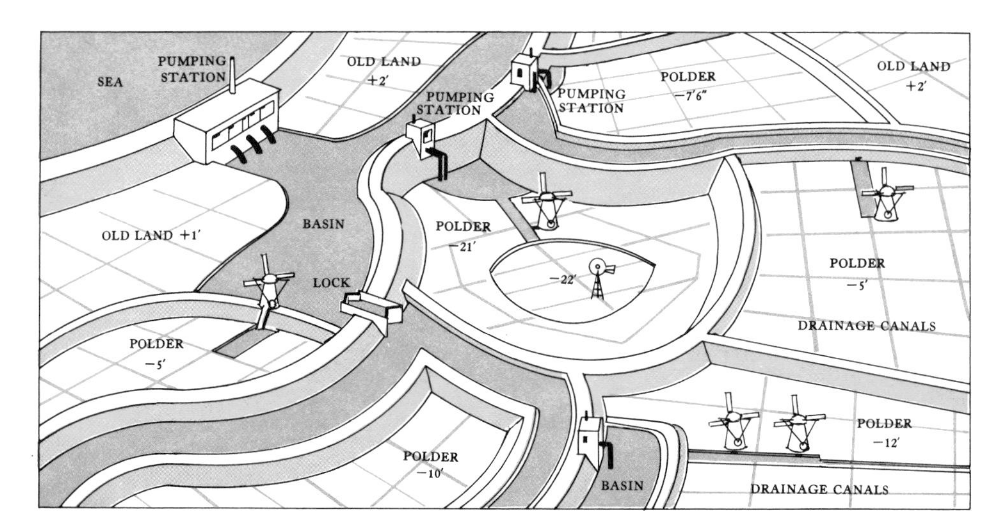

Seepage and rain water not thrown directly into the sea or into a river flowing to sea have to be lifted laboriously out of the country in successive stages. Not all polders have a direct connection with either sea or river; their surplus water is pumped into holding basins or boezems. The above diagram shows how polder levels differ: one polder may have been a reclaimed marsh or shallow sea area, the next a relatively deep lake. The + and − indicate the height above or below mean sea level. Bottom: the polders around Amsterdam in 1750. Although the city has expanded and its streets cover most of them today, they are still there, and are kept dry by pumping as they have been for centuries. Most of these invisible city polders no longer have their own polder boards but are governed by the city council. Sea dikes, lake and sea polders are ruled by a Waterschap; river dikes and river polders by a Hoogheemraadschap.

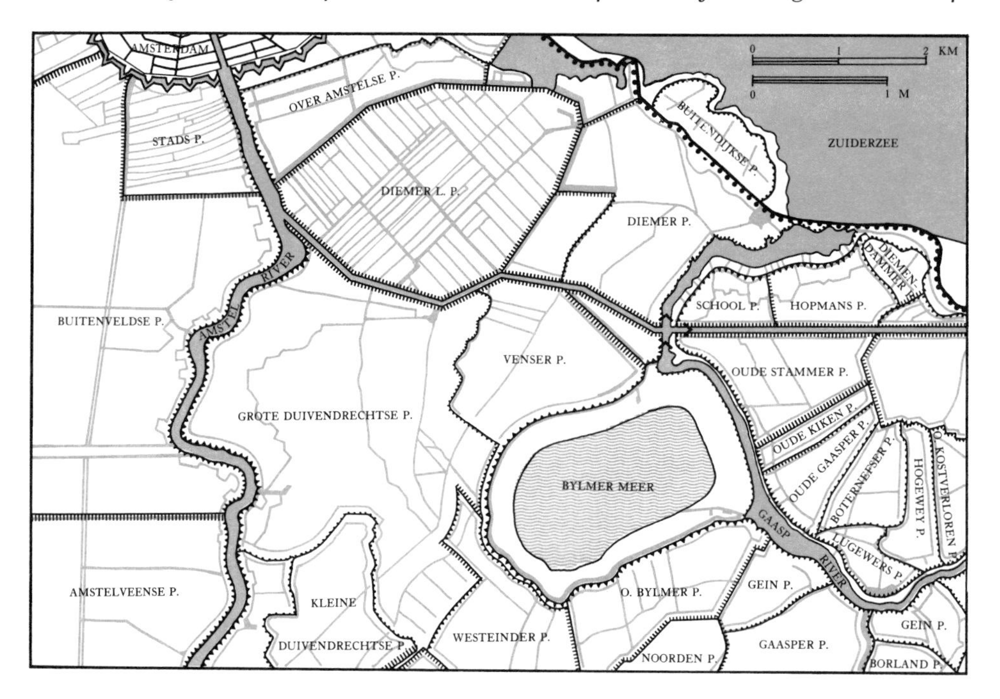

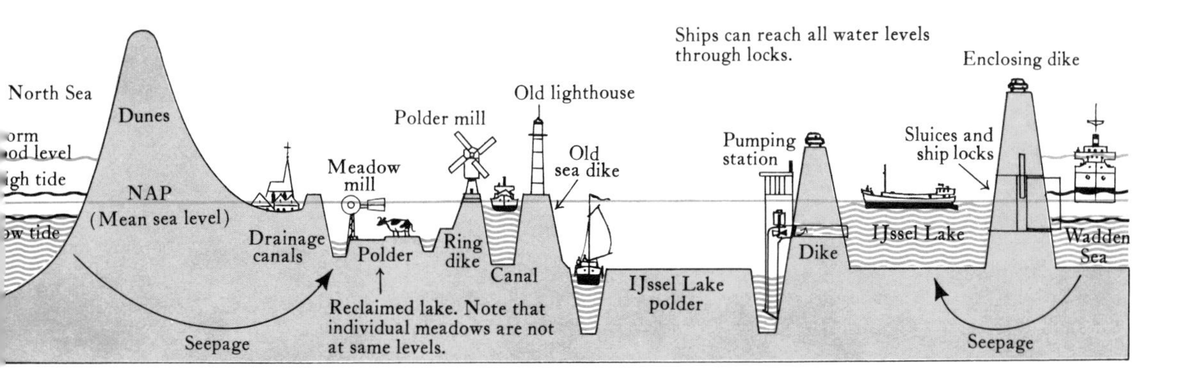

A slice of Holland! It goes without saying that this diagram is the ultimate in oversimplification.

to be strengthened and heightened all the time. The rising water is also constantly increasing the pressure against the dikes. It doesn't look as if the Dutch will ever be able to relax and take it easy.

Ever since the creation of the office of Director General of the Nation's River and Sea Works in 1754, Waterstaat has directed and led the nation's hydraulic endeavors. And it is one of the most important departments of the Dutch government. It is almost a state within the state, and organized much the same way. Head of State and Commander-in-chief is the Minister of Waterstaat. His cabinet consists of hydraulic engineers, and the scientists who are planning for centuries to come, are his general staff. The superbly trained professional army is made up of countless dike workers, lockgate keepers, and watermillers.

The good ship Holland has many thousands of watertight compartments, the polders (Zeeland alone has more than 350 of them). A polder is a self-governing body. The twelve members of a polder board—sometimes less—are elected by their neighbors. A dike council is organized in the same fashion, and the chairman is called the Dike Count, or Dike Reeve. These boards are like town councils and on them you will find farmers, the local doctor, the butcher, the greengrocer, or the dominee.

Some polders are so large that they rank as a Waterschap in themselves; smaller polders are joined together to form a Waterschap. Today there are more than 2800 of these ruling bodies. A Waterschap (sometimes they are called a *Hoogheemraadschap*) is in turn governed by an elected senior council headed by its own Dike Count, or *Hoogheemraad.* These boards have broad powers and are responsible to their provincial government, which reports directly to Waterstaat.

Polder board: Waterschap: Provincial government: Waterstaat. It goes without saying that this is an oversimplification of an intricate chain of command that is far more complicated in reality. The male population

The bar-lined Zeedijk, part of Amsterdam's sailor's-quarter, is an old sea dike which keeps the IJ River's water out of the city. A short time ago city work crews broke up the asphalt and streetcar tracks of the Sarphatistraat, a busy shopping street, in order to replace some old sewers. While digging, the workmen came upon a heavy layer of clay and immediately called the Department of Parks: "We found some good clay. Come and get as much as you want. The only condition is that you refill the hole with sand because we must finish the job by tomorrow." The delighted city-gardeners carted many truckloads away, then filled the excavation with sand. A few days later complaints by countless angry home owners whose basements were inexplicably flooding began to reach the town hall. At first no one knew the answer to this mystery, but upon

further study, it was discovered that the Sarphatistraat was actually part of the ring-dike of the Overamstelse polder. By taking away the clay, the buried but still active dike had been breached and the polder was slowly flooding! The clay was put back in and further damage was prevented. Pumps quickly lowered the water to its correct level. Automatic pumps are used in the cities and few would suspect their presence under manhole covers in busy streets. City polders have to be even more carefully controlled than others, for the accidental lowering of their water table would cause the soil to shrink and result in the sinking of every building in the polder. The importance of city polders' maintenance can be judged by the fact that the city polder board's authority supersedes that of any other city department, everywhere in the Netherlands.

within the jurisdiction of a Waterschap is registered in the Dike Army and can be called up on the Dike Count's orders in times of danger. Whenever a man plans to be absent from his Waterschap for an extended period of time, he has to ask his dike council for permission to leave.

The small cozy room off the main public room in The Golden Carp—the local inn—is filled with men, and with smoke; cups of steaming coffee stand on the table. In the old-fashioned potbellied stove a fire of peat is burning. On the wall, between beer ads and posters for animal feed, hangs a large detailed polder map, dotted with numbers and elevation measurements. Around a small table sit twelve men. After the weather, the price of milk, and the events of the day have been thoroughly discussed, the chairman calls the meeting to order.

The polder board is meeting today!

". . . Mr. Dike Count, I noticed last week that the dike near van Dalen's land needs some looking after. His cows have trampled the soil quite a bit again . . . no, it's not serious yet, but the next heavy rain will cause damage. The wooden casing should really be renewed. Yes, I'll speak to him about it."

". . . Jan Tromp called me last night to tell us that the old lock is causing trouble again. We had the carpenter out there now several times this year. We really cannot complain though, it was built in 1754! No, sir, it will have to be replaced. I have the quotation for the Waterschap right here. . . ."

"Grietje," one of the men calls to the innkeeper's daughter, who is scrubbing somewhere in the back, "bring us another cup of coffee."

Fresh cigars are lit, and you can cut the smoke with a knife.

"Gentlemen, have you noticed what the wash from these pleasure boats with their outboard motors is doing to the shore near the old bridge? I've had some of the men fix it again and again. I'm afraid we'll have to impose a speed limit of two miles an hour between Oud's place and Klein's barn. . . ."

Everything concerning the water is discussed, big or small. Materials are requested and the monthly reports for Waterstaat are prepared.

"Say, Willem, while you're at it, ask them for some new shovels; the old ones have just about had it."

"By the way, we must not forget to have a look at Gerrit Edel's ditches. He's had two warnings now and if he has not cleaned and dredged them yet, we have no choice but to give him a stiff fine! . . . It's the only thing that will help; his old man was the same way."

"Let's have another cup of coffee before we go out, . . . Grietje!"

"Remind van Dieren that his dike tax for this year has not yet been paid. . . ."

Should you ever see a small group of earnest men slowly walking along a dike, looking over every inch of the ground, pointing at a spot where the water has scoured away some soil, or going into a huddle under the lee of an old windmill, you will know that it is a polder board quietly doing its job.

On stormy nights in days gone by, the Dike Reeve climbed out of his warm bed. He said to his wife, "Don't worry, dear; I'll be back in a while," saddled his horse and rode out into the night to look after his dikes. When a spot seemed in danger, he rode back into the polder, summoning the other members of the board and the farmers. Warning them—like Paul Revere on his lonely ride—of the impending threat. Everyone, armed with shovels, would rush at once to the weakening spot and spread large tarpaulins over that section of the dike. Then a close watch was kept for as long as the storm lasted.

In our day, the Count of the Dike still gets up when the wind howls outside, as generations of Dike Reeves before him did. He will say to his sleepy wife, "I'd better have a look, dear; don't worry," and pull on a pair of hip boots and oilskins. Then he will grab a flashlight, get on his bicycle or into his car, and go out to his dikes. If he finds a spot

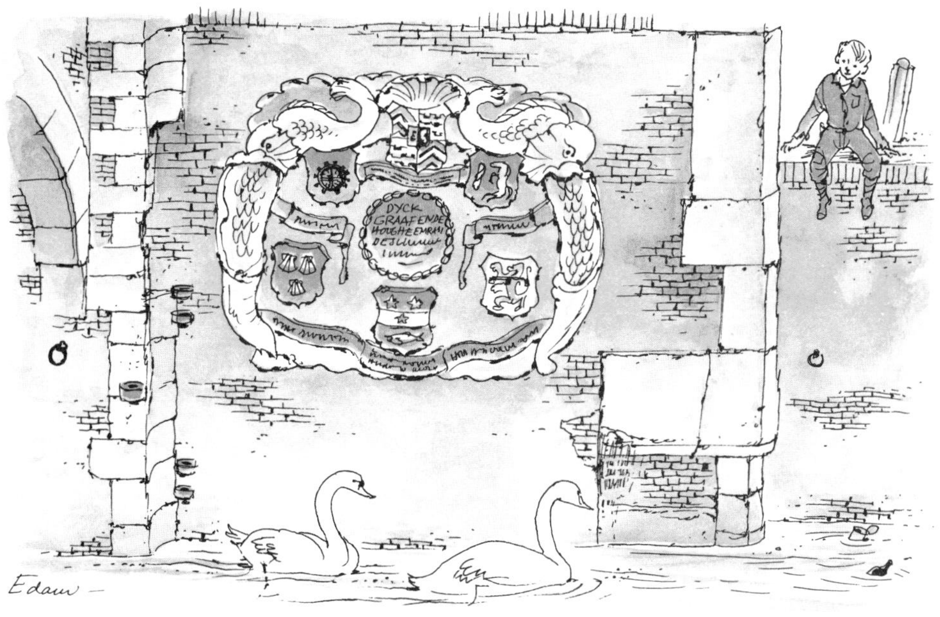

On some old locks and sluices there are elaborate commemorative stones, their coats of arms gaudily painted, gilded, or decorated with gracefully carved arabesque lettering: "In the Year of Our Lord 1795, Dike Reeve and Hoogheemraden of Kennemerland and West Friesland Ordered This Sluice Built to Turn the Water's Fury." There usually follows an appropriate Latin quotation and, always, the names of the members of the polder board. Those gentlemen never neglected the opportunity to remind future generations who was responsible for "The Wondrous Waterworks Against the Wrath of Oceanus and the Raging of Neptune."

in danger he will simply go to the nearest telephone and warn the others. They will then hurry out into the ice-cold night, as their ancestors have done for twenty centuries and as their children will do after them, for as long as there are dikes, storms, and the sea—as long as there is a Holland!

Throughout Holland you may see mysteriously marked posts standing at the water's edge. Sometimes you will find these marks painted on bridge foundations or chiseled into the slimy stone walls of an old sluice. Some will be brand-new, enameled on stainless steel, others carved into weathered oak long, long ago. But the markings are all identical and over them you will always find three letters—N.A.P. They stand for *Normaal Amsterdams Peil,* or Normal Amsterdam Level.

Until the seventeenth century no uniform method of measuring the water anywhere in the Lowlands existed. Towns and polders either used their own crude system or none at all. They pumped when their own land required it or merely when they felt like it. This made co-operation between polders, waterschappen, mills, and canals almost impossible. Then one day in 1681 an Amsterdam burgomaster decided that it was time to do something about it. He was going to determine the average high-tide level in Amsterdam's harbor! For a start he measured the water forty-eight times a day; after a few weeks he reduced the number of measurements to twenty-four a day. (And this is still being done today.)

The people of Amsterdam were at first rather suspicious when they saw their portly mayor, with his plumed hat and his starched white collar, performing a mysterious rite at the water's edge. "What the devil do you think he is up to, fiddling with those sticks in the harbor?" they must have asked each other. But the good burgomaster kept it up, and the people of Amsterdam got used to it in time. From then on, they merely shook their heads pityingly behind his back and said, "Too bad the old fellow has gone milling." Two years later his findings were completed and the mayor had workmen mark the high-water level with eight marble stones inscribed A.P. He did such an outstanding job that even with today's technical means it would be difficult to improve on his work.

At first the new measuring system was used only in and around the city, but it worked so well that it soon spread all over Holland and abroad as well. After 200 years it became necessary to bring the system up to date. This was mainly because Amsterdam's harbor now had lock gates and was no longer tidal. The settling of buildings and walls into

... and short ones!

which the old level marks had been carved also made the system less accurate than it had been. Rome was not built in one day and neither were the new measurements: N.A.P. finally reported for duty in 1926. Nine years later, Waterstaat, wisely planning ahead for centuries, carefully selected twenty-five locations all over the Netherlands where the geological formations would make changes in the level of the land highly unlikely. In these places, they buried concrete and granite N.A.P. markers as future references for unborn generations.

When the old A.P. that the mayor developed became N.A.P., the word PEIL was added on all gauges at precisely the point over which the water should not rise in that location. And this point may not be the same in every place. As soon as the water does rise beyond this level, pumping is begun. At the end of every Dutch news broadcast follows the weather report, and you may recognize the words "Amsterdam's Peil," for the latest and expected water-level forecasts are always an important part of it.

And so the Department of Waterstaat keeps a leaking Holland afloat, pumping, building new dikes and repairing old ones, making new land and planning for a thousand tomorrows.

The tide gauge of Schokland in the North East Polder, one that is no longer needed. To the right a section of the last remaining pole dike; early in WWII it was still intact but the desperate need for otherwise unobtainable materials forced Waterstaat to dismantle the pole dike and use the wood elsewhere.

XI

The blind eyes of the old harbor lights still look out over the sea—a sea of grass, that is. The two long jetties still stretch out their protecting arms around the harbor entrance, but there is no longer anything to protect. Sparrows hop between the dark canyons and crevasses of the great basalt blocks of the breakwater that lie along the jetties as if dropped by a playful giant. The harbor itself is bone dry and the ships have long since gone. Some rusty anchors, overgrown with weeds, lie half buried in the ground. Old chains and weathered ropes rest between the dandelions. From the high docks rotting mooring lines drop lifelessly down to the grass and on the quay rests a rich assortment of buoys, nets, and mildewed sails.

In the distance, where a farmer drives his tractor now, the fishing smack UK 67 was lost with all hands in the cold winter of 1924. High over the very spot where that hay baler is making such a racket, a small ship once sailed away to find a shorter route to the Indies: the *Half Moon* under a certain Captain Henry Hudson. This once was the Zuiderzee, the sea that was Holland's gateway to the world.

Leiden University was not quite twenty-five years old, Leeghwater had not yet written his *Haarlem Lake Book*, and another eight years would pass before work on the Beemster would even begin, when the first plan to reclaim the Zuiderzee was conceived. Around 1600 Henry Stevin—he was the son of Simon Stevin, who invented the sailing cart, decimal

fractions, and the parallelogram of forces—wrote an important book on the Zuiderzee in which he described what he thought should be done with it.

"First of all, the North Sea should be separated from the Zuiderzee by closing all the openings between North Holland, Texel, Vlieland, Terschelling and Ameland, connecting the last to Friesland. In these dams enough locks should be installed to enable ships to reach the North Sea, and also to shed water at ebb tide. It will then be possible to keep the Zuiderzee level always at that of the lowest tide. By never allowing sea water to re-enter, and since the rivers will keep on adding fresh water, the water of the Zuiderzee will turn fresh with the passing of time. Yes, and it will without any doubt offer much land to be diked in!"

We do not know how this prophetic and grandiose scheme was received. It had to remain wishful thinking because the technical means for such a gigantic undertaking simply did not exist.

"God's mills grind slowly but surely," say the Dutch and the idea was never wholly forgotten. When the Haarlem Lake was being reclaimed, engineers turned once again with boundless enthusiasm to the Zuiderzee, producing plans, plans, and more plans. In 1850 Waterstaat began to gather hydraulic data in earnest. In 1886 The Zuiderzee Society was founded to "investigate the possibilities for the reclamation of the Zuiderzee in the most thorough manner. The directors appointed Cornelis Lely, a thirty-two-year-old hydraulic engineer, to supervise the investigations. If ever the right man was chosen for the right job, he was it. Even so, the Society's directors would have been astounded had they known that Lely would not only become an eminent statesman, but the Minister of Waterstaat in three different cabinets.

Before the project could be started, there were several important questions to be answered: what are the soil and geological conditions? Not just a few feet down, but deep, deep below the bottom. Would it ever be possible, or even worth-while, to grow crops on the bottom of the old Zuiderzee? What would happen to the important IJssel River which

flowed into the Zuiderzee—would it silt up, causing inland floods and making navigation impossible?

In 1891, five years after his appointment, the Lely Plan lay on the desk of the Society's directors and the following year the main features were adopted by a state commission. Lely's plan, in short, called for the building of a gigantic dike across the mouth of the Zuiderzee—a short stretch between North Holland and Wieringen Island, the long stretch from the island's eastern tip to the Frisian coast—a total distance of twenty-seven miles! Once the dike was built, the sea would be a lake; there would be no tides to contend with and the lake could be reclaimed piecemeal.

As so often in the past, nature had to prod the Dutch into action. In January of 1916—twenty years after Lely's plan had been adopted by the state commission—the Zuiderzee smashed through the sea dike near Monnikendam and flooded a vast area. Amsterdam was saved only because the old IJ-sleeper dike north of the city held. A sleeper dike is a dike which is no longer on "active duty." When a dike no longer serves its original purpose it is rarely demolished. Instead, it is usually kept in repair and held in "reserve." The wisdom of this practice was proven again when this particular dike stood fast in 1960, providing the last obstacle between the area flooded in 1916 and the water, which this time attacked from the other direction.

The costly 1916 disaster brought the situation forcibly back into the public eye, but World War I was in full swing and the plan had to be shelved. Holland was neutral in that conflict, but the water had been let into the country and the fully mobilized Dutch sat it out behind their "Waterline."

In 1918 the Lely Plan became law. The newly formed Hydrographical Service of the Zuiderzee Works immediately began taking measurements, drilling thousands upon thousands of deep soil samples, and conducting important saline tests. Paramount, however, were the profound studies made of the water movements in and around the Zuiderzee. That same year

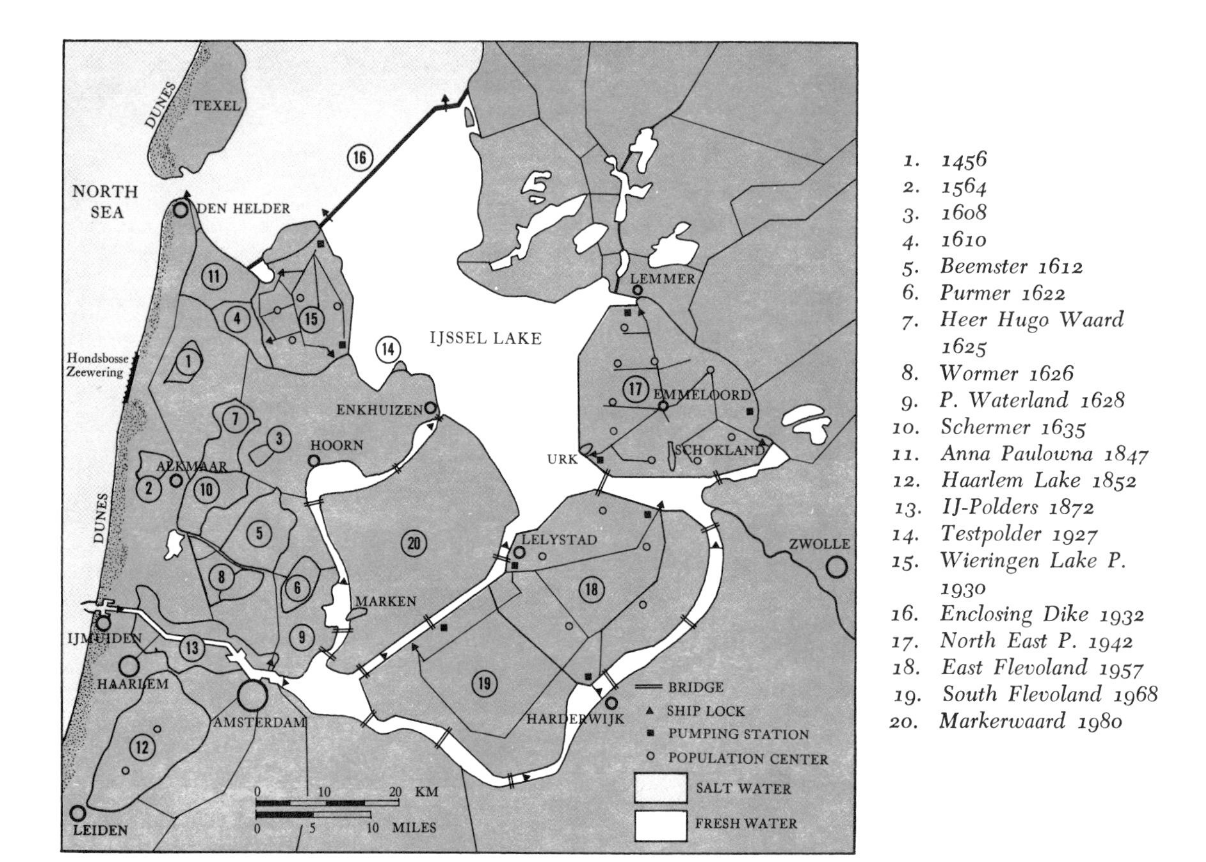

When the last Zuiderzee polder is reclaimed in 1980, the Netherlands will have grown in area by 10 per cent. Colonization and final work will not be completed until 2000.

the Lorentz Commission was created by the Dutch government. It was headed by H. A. Lorentz, who had won a Nobel prize in physics in 1902. Science had not stood still since Lely had collected his data in 1891, and these were now insufficient for Lorentz, who spent the next two years completing them. Between 1920 and 1926 the mathematical and tidal formulas were worked out. A most astonishing fact is that Holland at that time did not possess a Hydraulic Institute and so the famous German Institute at Karlsruhe was indispensable during those six years. In 1927 the now famous Delft Laboratories took over. One Waterstaat engineer called the final report of the Lorentz Commission "a monument of Dutch ingenuity." Another said, "He who wants to understand something of the Commission's report would have to devote a full year of his life to do so!"

The "easy" part of the task ahead was begun in 1923, building the dike linking Wieringen Island to North Holland: two miles in two years. In 1927 work on the big stretch was started by an army of men and machines. They began from two sides at the same time: a fleet of suction dredgers, barges, cranes, and tugboats—505 vessels in all—worked eastward from the Wieringen shore. A similar armada moved westward from the Frisian side. This was to be a super dike, twenty miles in length, running straight through the tides, straight through the open sea!

At the same time two artificial islands were built with emergency harbors, supply and fuel dumps. Huge willow and brushwood mattresses were woven—acres in size—and these were then pulled into position by powerful tugs. Once these "sinker pieces" were in position, barges loaded with stones came alongside. Then hundreds of men heaved the stones onto the floating willow mattress. When enough stones had been heaped on them, they sank and formed the sturdy foundation for the dike. Next, suction dredgers—enormous floating factories—pumped sand and boulder clay, taken from the sea bottom a good distance away, on top of the sinker piece. Thus, slowly, the dike emerged.

Enormous complexes of ship locks and sluices were finished beforehand because the water had to be controlled as soon as the dike would be completed. The work could not be allowed to interfere with Holland's vital shipping; hence, the ship locks.

In 1931 something curious happened. As a result of using too much wood, an unwelcome acquaintance showed up—the pile worm of old, the *Limnoria!* The use of wood was cut down and no further damage was done.

It was no job for quitters. In some places the waves swept fifty per cent of the sand away over and over again. The two dikes crept slowly

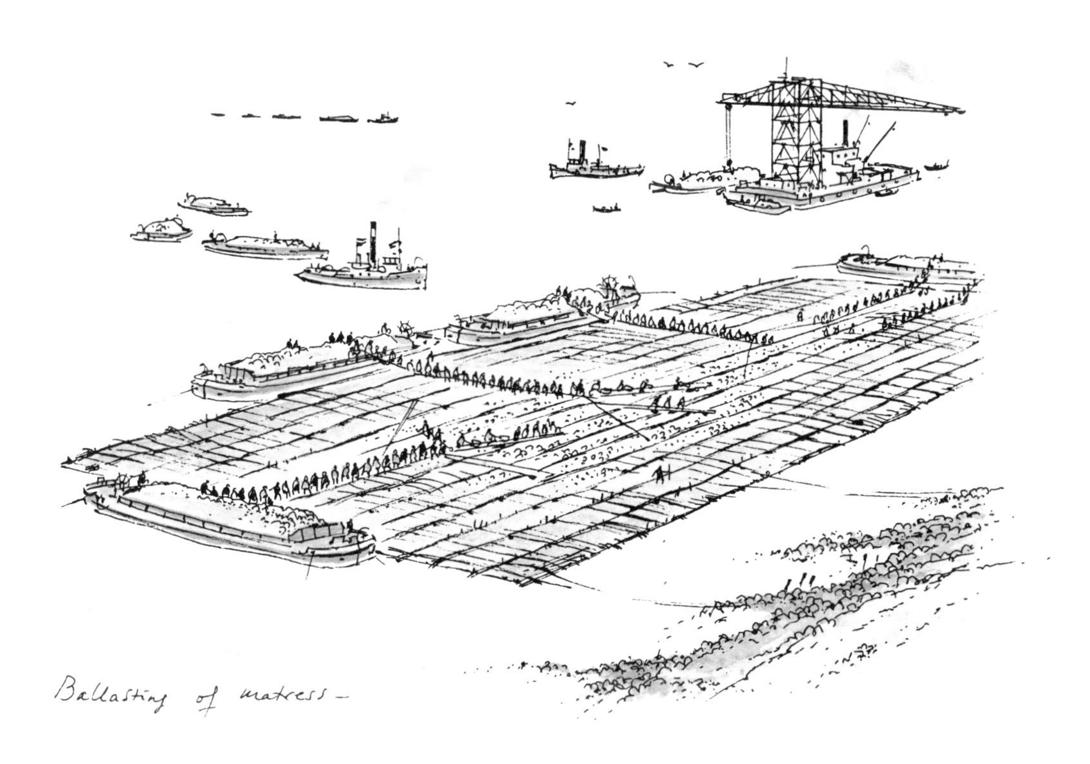

Ballasting of matress –

out to sea and after five years they were very close together—four miles east of Wieringen, sixteen miles west of Friesland. You can guess which stretch had been the most troublesome! But the scouring tides, pouring millions of tons of water through the narrowing opening four times every twenty-four hours, swept away stones, sand, and clay. The sea would not give up. It was only with the greatest difficulty, with one last Herculean effort, that De Vlieter (the Streamer), as the crews had nicknamed the gap, was closed. Still, it was touch and go. Like a general who at the critical moment decides to send his last regiment into battle, the Waterstaat engineers threw their slim reserves into the boiling opening—and won. When, on May 28, 1932, the last bit of clay slammed into the breach, sending muddy foam in all directions, whistles blew, flags were unfurled, and exhausted, muddy, unshaven men in hip boots yelled themselves hoarse. It was a great national occasion, the Dutch equivalent of "the driving of the Golden Spike."

After five centuries the Zuiderzee was a lake again—the IJssel Lake—and Holland's coastline had been shortened from 1200 to 1000 miles! The crown of the AFSLUITDIJK (Enclosing Dike) reaches a proud twenty-two feet above high water and measures a comfortable 600 feet at its base. It had taken 20,000,000 cubic yards of clay and 36,000,000 cubic yards of sand, not to mention the stones, to build that dike.

Numbers this vast usually have little meaning without a basis for comparison. The Pyramid of Cheops ought to do it: its contents measure 3,000,000 cubic yards, which means that the Dutch moved eighteen and two-thirds Great Pyramids in five years. And that's not bad at all.

Even before work on "the big one" began, Waterstaat built a sixty-acre test polder in a quiet corner of the Zuiderzee. It contained an experimental farm and a sophisticated laboratory for micro-biological research. Here so much favorable information was gathered and the experiments in general were so successful that it was decided not to wait for the completion of the AFSLUITDIJK, but to make a start on a large polder right away.

In 1929 the ringdike for the 49,000-acre Wieringer Lake Polder was begun. This dike curved from Wieringen Island south to Medemblik—which used to be the home town of our pagan friend Radbod. The dike was finished in 1930, and the first landmark to emerge from the waves was a big terp. This had been constructed underwater since it was much easier to dump the clay out of huge barges than to have to truck it in later on. It had long been an unanswered question whether there had ever been a Roman road this far north, leading to their garrisons in Germany. This question was answered once and for all when among the first objects found in the mud of the new polder were some Roman milestones.

By reclaiming the Zuiderzee, old problems were solved and new ones created. New employment had to be found for thousands of fishermen, for herring—their main catch—died in the brackish water of the lake. But flounders survived and miraculously adjusted themselves to their new environment, and the eels multiplied beyond belief.

Then, like a Biblical plague, the mosquitoes came. Billions and billions of them, swarming in dense black clouds over the water, moving in humming, dancing, ever-changing shapes over the surrounding land. There they clogged the radiators of moving automobiles and their remains ran greasily down windshields. The IJssel Lake was a perfect breeding

Fishing boats at their final resting place against the old shore of Wieringen Island in the polder. In the background the sluice complexes of the Enclosing Dike.

De Afsluitdijk - Salt water on left, fresh water on the right!

ground. "There, you see!" said the grim, Scripture-reading fishermen. "As we told you: Exodus 10:14–15! . . . AND THE LOCUSTS WENT UP OVER ALL THE LAND OF EGYPT AND RESTED IN ALL THE COASTS. . . . The Lord has justly sent us this visitation for tampering with His handiwork." But the mosquitoes were brought under control by destroying their breeding grounds.

I always look forward to crossing over the big dike with its great concrete sluice complexes and its long rows of massive steel doors hanging side by side like the blades in a row of enormous guillotines. No matter how often you have come this way, it is a small adventure every time. The trip really begins when you pass Radbod's grim brick castle at Medemblik, where it squats heavily on the edge of the IJssel Lake. A few hundred yards beyond, the road does something quite unexpected: it makes a sudden, sharp right turn through a notch in the almost vertical wall of the old sea dike, and then leaps down into the Wieringer Polder. The first object that catches the eye is a modern factory-like building straddling the new polder dike: the Lely pumping station. The roads are straight, fast, and uninteresting—until you recall that you are driving on the bottom of the sea. The trees are rather small and the farms you pass give a sense of well-being and prosperity. There is good reason for the trees not being any taller. In April 1945—three weeks before their surrender—the Germans blew up the dike and the polder was flooded. Everything in it was totally wrecked and every tree was killed. The Germans boasted that they could return Holland to the twelfth century if they felt like it. And this was by no means an empty threat.

Before you know it, the road rises and all of a sudden you are in an altogether different world. The trees are old, the road winds aimlessly, every farm is different, and in the village the ancient houses lean against

HOW A POLDER DIKE IS BORN

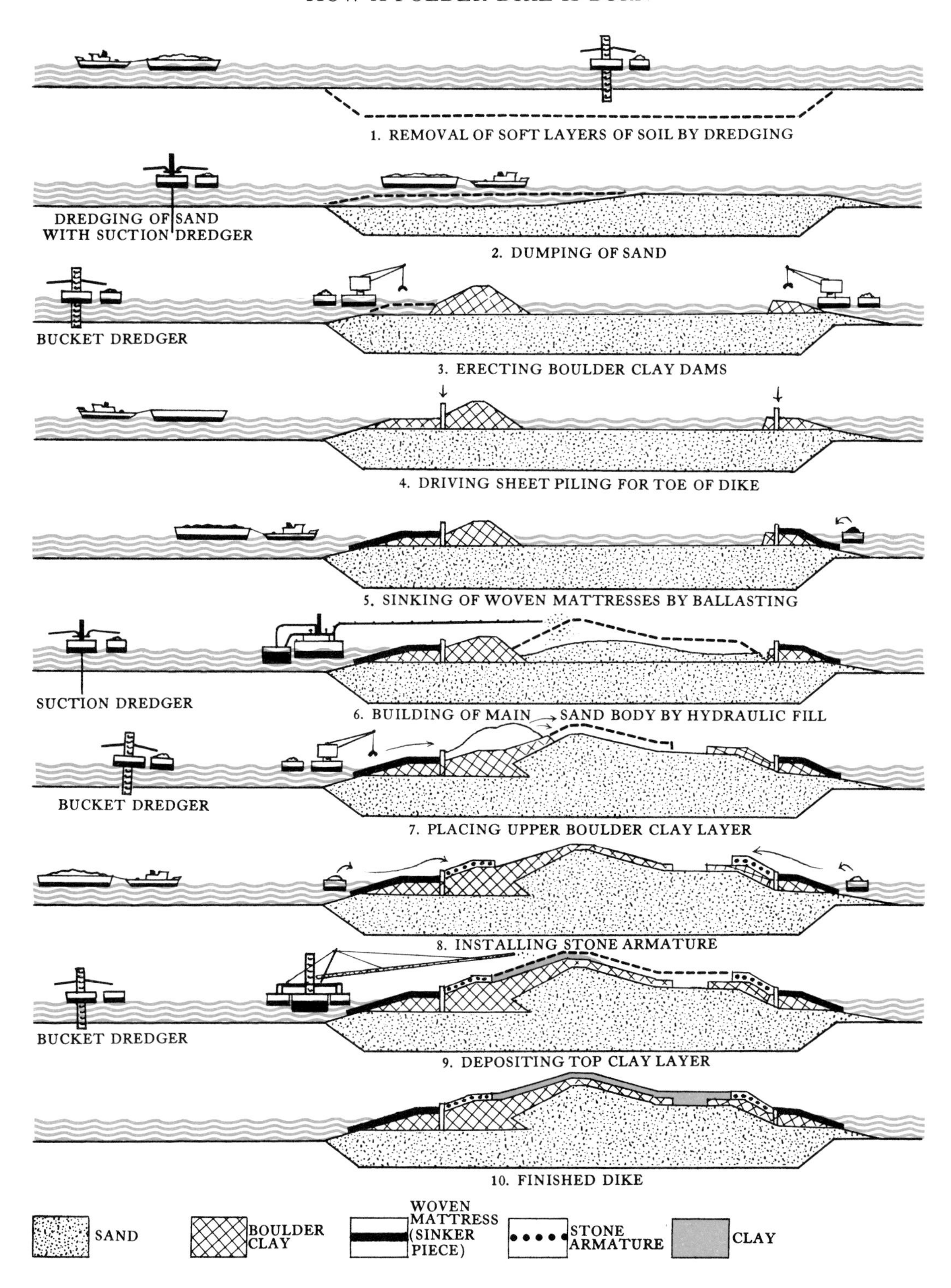

A dike is not just a simple earthen dam but a carefully engineered structure, designed for maximum strength, safety and efficiency in a specific location. The dike shown here is a Zuiderzee polder dike. A dike profile somewhere else might look totally different. (Drawn from Dienst der Zuiderzeewerken)

one another as if seeking comfort in sharing the past. Perhaps it is my imagination, but even the grass looks older here. No wonder—you are on Wieringen. The transition from the twentieth to the eighteenth century is so sudden that it hardly registers. It does not matter much, for five minutes later you leave the island for science-fiction surroundings: sluice complexes, bridges, and ship locks; a mechanical, steel, and concrete city of the future. This, too, flashes by, and then without warning you are out on the dike. The green embankment on the sea side is far too high to look across. But the lake on the other side is quite near; the waves seem to keep you company as they ride alongside. In the distance sail old fishing boats with tanned sails and leeboards, and water and sky blend in a shimmering haze where the horizon should be.

The road is heavily traveled and buses and trailer trucks thunder by. Over the spot where the dike was closed in 1932 stands a monument. You park your car and climb the simple tower. On a clear day a breathtaking sight awaits you: the sky, the sea, and the full length of the dike. To the west you see the coast of Holland and far, far away a thin blue pencil line, the Frisian coast. The salty sea wind blows hard in your face and you have the feeling of standing on the bridge of a tall ship. When you finally leave reluctantly, you pass an inscription carved into the stone at the foot of the stairs: A NATION THAT LIVES IS BUILDING FOR ITS FUTURE.

And the Dutch are very much alive!

Lely's Statue on the Afsluitdijk —

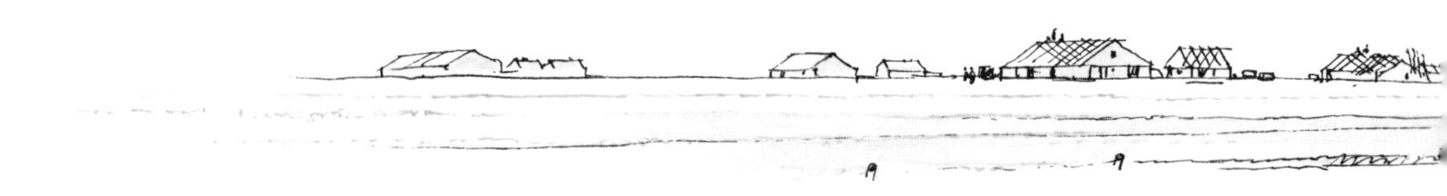

Oost Flevoland '68

XII

When World War II broke out in September 1939, the Dutch once more enlisted the water as an ally by activating the *Waterlinie,* flooding strategic areas with fresh river water. In World War I these areas had included parts of North and South Holland, the western half of Utrecht, and part of Gelderland and North Brabant. In 1939 the "New Dutch Waterline" consisted of a wide belt of water stretching from the IJssel Lake, south of Amsterdam, to the Biesbosch. The area behind it was the Fortress Holland (which included the big cities). There the Dutch relaxed. And why not? Their Waterline had never failed them and Amsterdam was still considered one of the most difficult fortifications to capture in the world.

But in the early morning of May 5, 1940, the Germans came and the water did not halt them. They came in airplanes that dropped paratroopers far behind the ring of bright water, and Holland was conquered in exactly five days.

After the successful invasion of Normandy in 1944, the Allies needed a deep-water port to supply their armies during the final assault on Germany. The big, well-equipped Belgian port of Antwerp had been liberated, but could not be used because the Germans still held the Zeeland island of Walcheren and from there controlled the entrance to the Scheldt River. Once again the water was enlisted to drive an enemy from Holland's soil. After warning the population of Walcheren the RAF bombed holes in the dikes. The inrushing water flushed the Germans out of their fortifications, and the road to Antwerp lay open. The war

Eastern Flevoland: the first crops of linseed and winter rye are in bloom, and pre-fab farms and barns are going up. The trees along the roads and in 5000 acres of young "forests" are only 2 feet tall . . . 100,000,000 pieces of drainage pipe have been laid (20,000 miles) and the total bill for hydraulic works, land development, colonization and public works came to $300,000,000!

lasted another seven months, and during that time the sea had a free hand with the island. It is believed that if the war had lasted through the fall of 1945 Walcheren would have been lost forever. Even so, the dikes were only repaired with exceeding difficulty.

Today, in the age of ICBMs and armored airborne divisions, the Waterline—like the crossbow and the cavalry charge—is a relic of the past. The Dutch will not have to cut their dikes again voluntarily, nor will they ever again be able to feel secure behind their Silver Fortress.

In 1936 a ringdike, thirty-five miles long, was built in the IJssel Lake, and in 1941 the bottom of the 119,000-acre North East Polder fell dry. The lessons from Haarlem Lake were well remembered, and every detail had been carefully planned ahead by teams of sociologists, psychologists, agricultural experts, educators, and the many other specialists without whom a modern society cannot function. Farms, villages, and a capital

Lely Stad 1968 - not quite, but almost all of it.
In a few years 30.000 people will live here!

were mapped. The exact locations of roads, sewers and even forests had been determined. Nothing had been forgotten. Only so many barbers, grocers, haberdashers, and bicycle repairmen were allowed to settle the new land at first; only as many as the land could initially support. The ratio: one city man to three farmers.

On the new land everything is done to make life as pleasant and "normal" as possible, to make it look "lived in," like the old land. The towns are laid out with streets that do not meet at right angles and not every house stands in line. Highways have built-in curves; here and there small woods are planted. All is done to avoid monotony and to create the illusion that these communities have developed organically over a long period of time. Again—as on the old land.

The government footed the astronomical bill and owns the new land. Farmers cannot buy, but lease their model farms from the government for twelve years. The lease can be renewed if the farmer works his land well—almost a certainty, since each man is selected with the greatest care out of 300 to 400 applicants for each farm!

Dutch farms are small and can in general support only one family. This means that when a farmer has three sons, only one of them can expect to take over the place some day. For this reason many farmers' sons are drawn to the reclamations and toil on the dikes instead of leaving the land and moving into the city. For he who has helped to create the new land (or his orphans!) has the preferred right to a farm in the new polder.

In the 1970s the last of five enormous polders will have been carved out of the IJssel Lake, more than half a million acres. These will jointly form Holland's twelfth province: Flevoland. A capital has been founded

After 7 months of pumping, South Flevoland's 150,000 acres were declared officially dry on May 30, 1968. "Isn't it a beautiful sight?" said one engineer leaning on a now silent pump and pointing at the bleakness of gray ooze and mud. "We only stopped pumping once, on Christmas day. Whatever you do, don't get off the dike! Quicksand everywhere. See that 'copter? Sowing reeds to fight the growth of weeds. Oh, what a beautiful sight . . ."

in eastern Flevoland (133,000 acres) on the bottom of the old sea. It is called Lelystad—Lely town!

"I had never been in one of the new Zuiderzee polders," a KLM pilot told me some time ago, "but I've seen East Flevoland grow! I flew over it twice a week, going to New York and coming back. Every time we looked the dikes were longer. Then these were closed and the pumping started. Nothing happened at first. Then one day—we were coming in low and the sun was setting—I said to the captain: look at those strange dark spots in the water! That was the first land! After that there was more of it every week. Noah must have seen something like it from way up on Mount Ararat."

The first lands to appear above the waves in a new polder will become the cemeteries. So that the dead can later be buried well above the water table, suction dredgers deposit sand and clay under water in these prearranged places before the pumping has even begun. The large canals for drainage and for navigation are dug under water, too (it's easier to dredge than to dig later).

When the last water has been pumped out of the new polder by modern pumping stations at a clip of 375,000,000 gallons a day, the sea bottom lies bare, a wasteland of deep puddles, ooze, and mud. Nothing stirs. There is absolute silence, the silence of space, the quiet of a battlefield after the battle. Soon the soil dries out, great cracks appear in the ground, and the first few hardy leaves of grass and camomile raise their heads. The wind has carried flower seeds from faraway fields, and soon a gay blue or yellow speck blooms hopefully amidst desolation. The grass spreads fast, and, when there is enough to eat, the first inhabitants arrive—hares, lots of them.

And so the population increases, bugs and beetles crawl over the old dike, down into the new land. In the spring duck and pheasant nestle where the flounders spawned only last year, and honking geese fly where once schools of herring swam. During that spring man, too, has been busy in the new polder. He has crisscrossed it in jeeps and trucks, inspecting and taking soil samples. The surveyors have been around as well: thousands of numbered red and white poles stand like peppermint-stick sentries wherever you look. They indicate the positions of farms and roads. Everything is peaceful, the clover is in bloom, and millions of loudly humming honeybees dart from one flower to the next.

Then one day this pastoral peace is rudely shattered. Huge throbbing steel monsters climb across the old dike, clanking and rumbling with pounding Diesels through clover and fragrant camomile—an army of giant bulldozers, draglines, and ditch diggers. Soon arrow-straight ditches reach to the far horizon; these are connected to small canals which, in turn, run into larger canals and from these the pumping stations can throw all the rain and rising ground water into the lake. Now the land can be kept dry. In the North East Polder alone 12,000 miles of ditches were dug and many more thousands of miles of canals. Ships with building materials, concrete, and structural steel busily ply the canals. In the fields huge plows tear deeply into the fertile soil. Not far behind follow harrows and strange self-propelled machines that lay mile after mile of drainage pipe, for oats and barley must soon be planted!

If you drive behind the old, lazily curving sea dike—reaching up a full thirty feet—you would never even suspect that there is no longer a sea on the other side of that high green wall. For on top of the dike stand

South Flevoland, May 1968. The water is gone and fishermen are taking down their nets and hauling their work boats across the dike into IJssel Lake, where their ship is riding

beacons and lighthouses and the towns and villages still smell of tar and tides. They still bear the indelible mark of the sea. This is Holland: flat, fertile meadows with rows of stately trees, old weathered farms with moss-overgrown tile roofs, quiet canals lined by swaying reeds and willows. Cows contentedly chew their cuds, swift swallows skim low over the water, and a blue egret stands motionless on one stilt leg between the water lilies. A horse whinnies behind a barn and you hear the clanging of milk cans, the cackling of chickens and in the distance a train whistle. This is the old land. Then all of a sudden the road rises and you are on top of the dike, fully expecting to see whitecaps and fishing smacks with rusty tanned sails, fully expecting to smell the sea. . . . Startled, you hold your breath, for before you lies the New Land, reaching as far as the eye can see, dissolving in a distant sky—and you drive down onto the bottom of the sea. . . .

You have entered a new world. Here the land is flatter, the grass is greener, and the sky is taller than on the other side of the dike. Everything you see is new, the farms with their clean orange tile roofs, the freshly painted bridges, and the still spotless concrete ribbons of the roads. This is a bright young land risen from the waves—empty, seemingly endless—a land where no tree is taller than twelve feet (they were planted only last year!).

Fifteen minutes later you enter a brand-new, noisy town smack in the middle of the polder. Planners and architects have managed to give this town the old-time look. The church is the focal point around which the houses cluster. It's market day and hundreds of people mill around the canvas-topped stalls. Everything is for sale, from smoked eels to long woolen underwear, from bicycle tires to cooing pigeons crowded to-

at anchor. In time they will have to move again, for by 1980 the Markerwaard will also be finished and only a canal will remain between the two polders.

gether in their willow baskets. There is great variety in the people as well. There are tall, blond Frisians and red-cheeked, dark women from Zeeland, almost hidden behind their large lace caps and uncounted layers of skirts. There are people wearing somber costumes from Urk and others the colorful dress of Hindeloopen. The population of the new land is made up of people from all over Holland.

Houses and stores have been built in different styles and a variety of materials has been used: traditional gabled roofs next to the functional lines of a modern one. There is a single traffic light in the main street, and a rusty anchor behind the service station. Through the school's open windows floats the sound of children singing. From all around come the noises of life: laughter, motors, hammering, and the crying of a baby born on the new land.

On the way out of town you pass a silent cemetery, still empty, with only a few new lonely headstones huddling together in a far corner of the fresh green lawn.

Urk ceased to be an island when the dike of the North East Polder linked it to the mainland. The island's austere population had preserved its ancient customs and costumes through centuries of isolation. Their fundamental religion was in the best "fire and brimstone" tradition.

Shortly after World War II, we took a trip around the old Zuiderzee,

Urk —

mainly to show the sights to our elderly guest, Mrs. P. She was English and no one could possibly mistake her for anything else with her mannish-looking hat, solemn suit of tweeds, and heavy walking shoes. She wore no make-up except for a barely noticeable touch of lipstick. I have never seen a less frivolous apparition. When we passed Lemmer on a Sunday afternoon, we noticed that the road leading into the polder had just been opened to traffic that morning, and I believe we were among the first motoring "foreigners" seen in Urk.

As we drove slowly onto the island, the local population quickly made us feel at home by throwing small stones at our car while yelling: "It's the Lord's Day! The Day of Rest! . . . Have ye forgotten that it is the Sabbath?"

We immediately drove out of range, parked the car, and re-entered this bulwark of righteousness on foot. For a while all went well, but soon we were being followed by a cluster of small, grim children in wooden shoes, dressed in their black Sunday best.

Cosmetics were unknown on Urk in those days and Mrs. P.'s almost invisible lipstick must have been the first seen by the islanders. The children, fresh out of Sunday school, began to chant something behind our backs, and it was plainly directed at Mrs. P. "Whore of Babylon, Great Whore of Babylon!" they cried at poor Mrs. P., who asked, "What are those dear, dear children saying?" We explained that it was the customary greeting—a kind of Urk "Aloha"—and were on our way. Sooner than we had planned.

There is one place in the North East Polder where you will see a long, irregular shape rising up unexpectedly from the old bottom of the sea. This was the island of Schokland—a landlocked island now! On it sits the old village, a weatherbeaten lighthouse, and clumps of ancient wind-bent trees.

Schokland was once a prosperous and much bigger island with several sizable towns. On one end was a large and well-known abbey. The sea had always been particularly vicious when attacking Schokland, and, as a result, it had been steadily shrinking. In 1573 a winter storm drowned most of the island and, when the storm had finally died down, meadows, whole towns, and the abbey had disappeared below the waves. Ever since that day, fishermen said that if you sailed on a quiet night over the spot where the abbey once stood and listened closely you could still hear its bell ring!

In 1941 the sea around Schokland fell dry. On the site of the abbey bricks and bits of pottery were found. And a church bell buried deeply in the sand. In the steeple of a church hangs the old bell, singing out loud where no chimes had been heard for almost 400 years—except, of course, by the fishermen at night—ringing out at the top of its voice over the reborn land!

XIII

When you hear the word archaeology you think of Egypt, Greece, or Italy—Holland would almost certainly be the last country that you would think of. Still, archaeologists have always been busy in the Netherlands. In the sand dunes they looked for the remains of the earliest settlers. On the sites of the old Roman forts, coins, corroded swords, and helmets have been dug up. Domburg in Zeeland was a Roman ferry port to England and here one can sometimes find the remnants of little statues the legionnaires threw into the sea to put Neptune in a good mood before crossing the dangerous North Sea. Some of the finds have been very surprising, even spectacular—about forty years ago a Viking ship was dug up under a house in Utrecht, today a distance of twenty miles from the IJssel Lake.

Most terpen have been examined and, as a result, we know how the mound dwellers lived, what they ate, and what they fought with. The terpen are like historical layer cakes: at certain levels Roman beads and pottery were found, at others Frankish implements. This made accurate dating possible.

To most of us the empty desolation of a new polder offers few—if any—attractions. But, to the archaeologist, it is paradise. When the last water was pumped out of the Wieringen Polder, archaeologists set out on a successful treasure hunt. They found skeletons of gray whales that swam here 20,000 years ago, mammoth teeth, crude stone spearheads with which the mammoths were hunted, and tools from the Stone and Bronze ages.

In the former machine shop at Ketelhaven, East Flevoland, it always rains. Fine spray from pipes and garden hoses, lying about like spaghetti spilled on the kitchen floor, falls on an incredible collection of parts of ancient ships and old wood to keep them from shrinking. "That big piece is the bow of a Hansa caravel," explains the supervisor, "that hollow log in front of it, a dugout from 250 B.C." The hall is filled with rows of rudders, carved lions ("from an East India Man"), guns and anchors, all found in the polders. The storerooms hold drawers and boxes filled with thousands of items: 15th-century toys, perfectly preserved medieval baby booties, rolls of leather, tools, crucifixes, spoons, swords and jewelry. "There would be enough to open a store and have every department well stocked." (Top right): This B-17 never returned from a mission over Germany during WWII. So far 12 planes have been found in South Flevoland. (Bottom right): "This one is not going to be interesting," workman W. said as he stopped digging. "I can tell by now. The last one though! It was burned pitch black in the bow, and the planking was full of plugged holes. A mystery, mijnheer! It turned out to be a fireship, shot full of holes and used more than once!"

Near Wieringen more Roman artifacts were discovered, as well as pre-medieval sandstone coffins and the foundations of a hamlet drowned in 1334.

But what are found most often are wrecked ships. In the North East Polder alone, more than 160 wrecks have been discovered. Not much attention had been paid to the eighteen wrecks found in the Wieringen Polder. They interfered with plowing, and were dug up and thrown away. Things are done differently today.

The oldest vessel found in the North East Polder was a primitive dug-out. The others date from 1200 up to 1932. Only ships that sank recently can be spotted above the ground. Most ships that came to grief sank into the soft sediment on the bottom and came to rest on the solid clay underneath. The passing tides gently heaped more and more silt over the wreck, as if trying to conceal and preserve their newly won trophies.

From these ships historians have learned a great deal. Their cargoes provide information about early trade and economy; their cabins yield clues as to how the old sailors navigated, lived, and worked; their hulls tell historians how ships were built at certain times. Most of the wrecks are discovered when the deep canals and drainage ditches are dug. Only the ones that sank still deeper have not been found. Not many are missed, though. The drainage ditches are only twenty-four feet apart and few wrecks can slip through this closely woven net. Even so, a man living in one of the new polders may be one of the few people in this world who can find a shipwreck in his potato patch.

Once a wreck has been located it is excavated with the aid of the most

advanced scientific methods, carefully measured, and photographed at all stages of the work. Then a detailed drawing is made, showing every rusty nail. The hull is usually full of sand and silt, the wood mostly in poor condition, making it impossible to salvage the ship in one piece. First, it is laid completely bare, then slowly taken apart piece by piece. The most common clues as to when the ship was lost are coins, potsherds, and tobacco pipes. The method of construction will tell only when it was built, not when it sank, for these sturdy wooden ships sometimes lasted for more than a hundred years!

Unfortunately, it is impossible to preserve the ships in one piece, but the most interesting fragments are preserved and go into storage. Their cargoes vary as much as their shapes: from large men-of-war to modest fishing smacks.

"Oh no, we haven't gone into all the wrecks yet," you may be told by the officials of the Archaeological Section of the Zuiderzee works. "We're taking our time—couldn't handle 'em all at once anyway. Besides, they'll stay in good condition in the ground and we know where to find them!"

"It's a shame you were not here last year; we found an interesting one—had her hold full of buckwheat. Another close by carried 500 bricks, which were used to build convents and castles in the fifteenth century."

In fishing boats the fish bones will tell what types of fish were commercially caught: mostly herring and huge codfish. In the smaller ones you may expect to find only the few simple belongings of three poor sailors: a bone spoon, some pots, and maybe some copper coins. But coasters and river boats usually carried the skipper and his whole family, as they still do today. What you find in these boats gives a startling, intimate view of life on board a fifteenth-century freighter, for here you have a complete medieval household! The captain's wife's prize pewter may still rest in a muddy cupboard, and the skipper's clay pipes and the buttons of his coat are around somewhere; all the simple daily things . . . a small crucifix and some children's toys.

Sometimes you find a tragedy under the sand. In wreck W 98, a *tjalk* (freighter) that went down in the 1760s, a skeleton was found caught in the half-opened forward hatch . . . the bones of the ship's dog were still chained in the main cabin. That one must have gone down fast. . . .

Or it may be a more recent drama: an RAF Lancaster bomber or an American Flying Fortress that never returned from a World War II mission over Germany, the remains of the pilot strapped in his unused parachute.

A sixteenth-century wreck was found to contain stone blocks from the west coast of Denmark that were used to reinforce dikes. Until then it was not known that these stones were imported at such an early date.

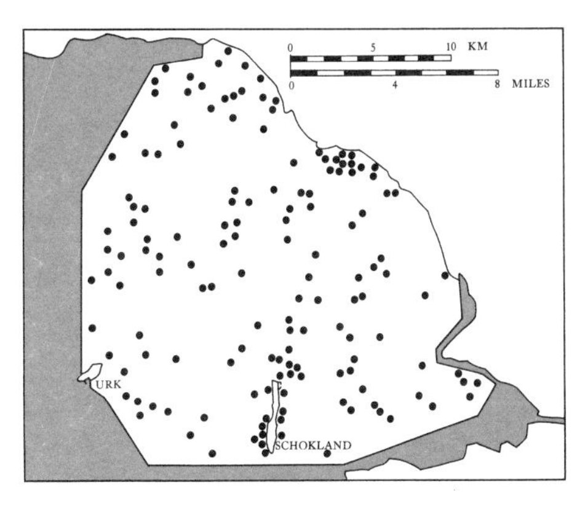

These are the shipwrecks found in the North East polder. By June 1968 more than 100 wrecks had been discovered in East Flevoland and the hunt for more continued. What is hidden in the old sea bottom of South Flevoland will be known in the near future. More will be found when the great Markerwaard falls dry in 1980. In that area many sea battles took place and the main shipping lane to the North Sea also ran here.

Nearby two skeletons were discovered, one still wearing his leather boots and the other clutching a purse filled with copper coins dated before 1586.

Sometimes archaeologists come across a riddle: once they found several half ships. Nobody had any idea what could have happened to them. Then it was discovered that certain ships were sometimes used to tow larger vessels and when the towing ship was old it occasionally pulled itself cleanly in two pieces—even lengthwise.

I was told the following story some time ago, but have been unable to verify it. On the other hand, it is too romantic not to relate, so let's hope that it is true.

A few years ago the wreck of a large ship was found. It had sunk in the sixteenth century and its hold was filled with hewn sandstone blocks. The cargo was unloaded and the experts had a hunch that they had been intended for a church or monastery. It was an educated guess, because this type of stone was then mainly used for this purpose, and the shape of the pieces indicated this as well. Then the detective work began. It was quickly discovered that the stones came from a Norwegian quarry—but where were they bound for? Who had ordered them?

After looking through the archives, letters of inquiry were sent to old churches and religious institutions all along the coast of the old sea. It was a long shot, but one day the search was crowned with success. A letter arrived from a monastery in the city of K, wherein the Brother Archivist reported, "We indeed ordered a quantity of sandstone blocks in 1549 hewn to our following specifications. [There followed the list: so many cornerstones, so many lintels, so many posts, etc.] The aforementioned materials were intended to build an addition to our chapel. P.S. Our order was never received."

The unloaded cargo was checked against the Brother Archivist's list, and, sure enough, it was all there. A few days later some heavy trucks rumbled to a stop in front of the monastery. The long-lost order had reached its destination. The order arrived a bit late, almost four centuries, but the goods were safely delivered. The story has a poetic conclusion: the monastery's chapel has a brand-new addition, built with some very old blocks!

SCHOKLAND IN 1938 AND TODAY.

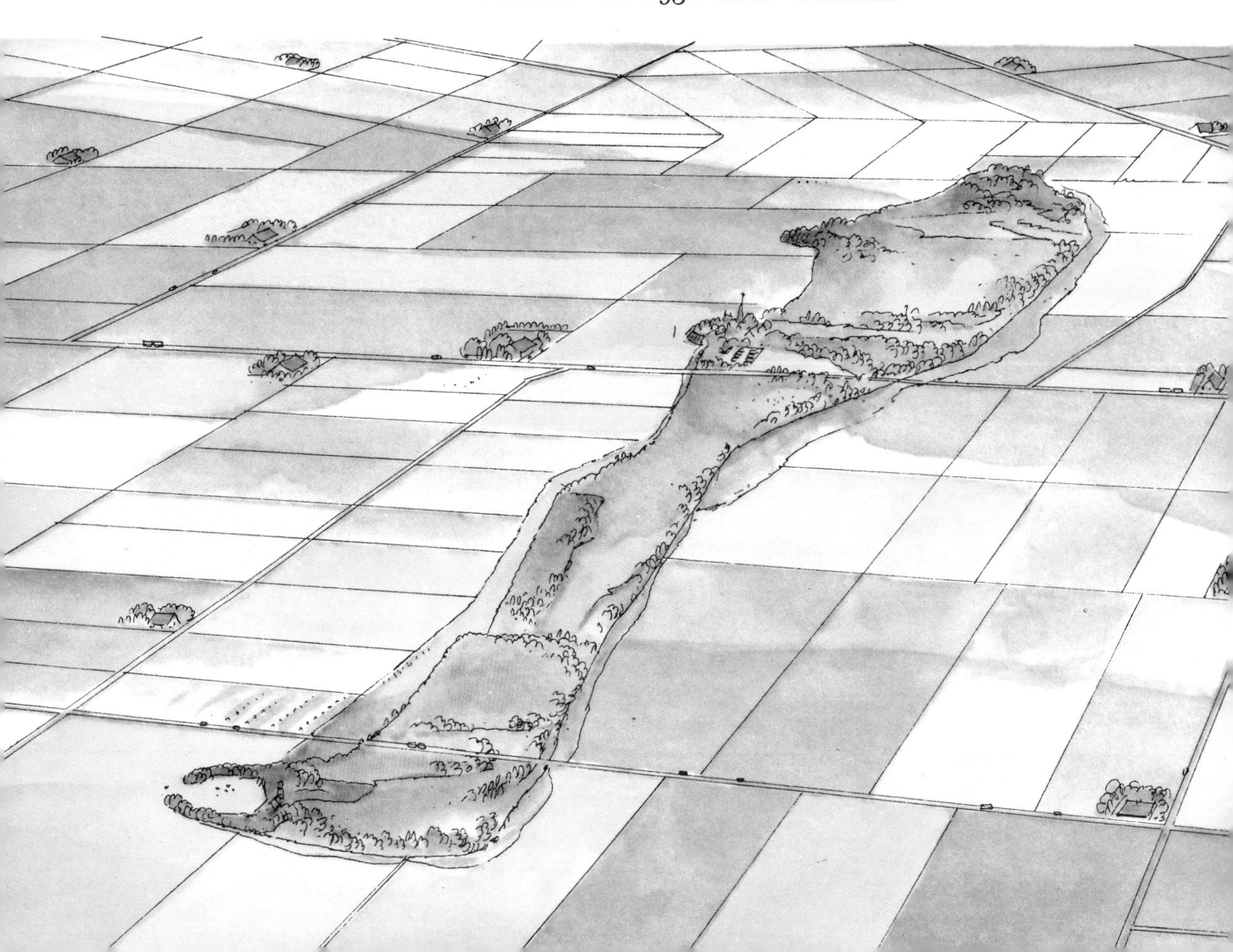

XIV

Progress has its price, and that price was the loss of the Romance of the Zuiderdee. It is almost impossible to describe the beauty, the charm, and the unique variety of the old Zuiderzee. For around it no town or village was alike, the costumes worn differed everywhere, and even the ships were unlike those of other places.

Colorful Marken is no longer an island. Here there were only a handful of family names—Kapitein, Schipper, Admiraal—since the people had always intermarried. Their houses were built on high pilings to be safe when the water rose. When you tied up your boat in the inner harbor, the old peg-legged harbor master in three-quarter breeches appeared as if by magic to extract a modest tribute for setting foot on the island. (He is probably doing the same thing in the municipal parking lot now.)

Across the water is Volendam—where people wear what much of the world erroneously believes to be Holland's national costume. The men dress in baggy pants with large silver buttons, and the women wear striped skirts and peaked lace caps with pointed flaps.

A few miles to the north there's sleepy, unspoiled Edam, where a carillon sings out the hours over the old town.

Magnificent Hoorn, once mighty Enkhuizen, Medemblik.

Harderwijk, Huizen, and regal Kampen. . . . A nostalgic roll call of great ports that are ports no longer, the faintly glittering jewels set in the winding green necklace of the Lost Sea.

The Dutch, fully aware of what is being lost in folklore and tradition, are very anxious to preserve memories of the old way of life and so

Enkhuizen
VD 86
VD 104
UK 23
Volendam

H 112
Hoorn

founded the Zuiderzee Museum in Enkhuizen. The main building is the Peperhuis, the seventeenth-century pepper warehouse of the East India Company, where, if you probe with a pencil in between the enormous floorboards, you can dig up some 300-year-old peppercorns! In the harbor rides a seaworthy fleet of old Zuiderzee ships that are part of the collection.

Holland's best-known legend is that of "the Lady from Stavoren." Stavoren, once a thriving seaport, is today a dreary little town on the Frisian coast. Its demise as a port was due to a sand bar that grew across the harbor entrance so that sea ships could no longer enter. The sand bar is called *Het Vrouwezand,* The Woman's Sand.

In the seventeenth century Stavoren was a booming, busy port and no one was richer than the Lady from Stavoren, who owned more ships and warehouses filled to bursting than anyone in the city. But her arrogance and greed grew with her wealth. One day she summoned her best captain and ordered him "Take your ship and bring me back the noblest, richest cargo that you can find in the world. I do not care how long it takes you to find it, or what it will cost, but I want the best!" A few months later the returning ship was sighted and the lady immediately went down to the harbor where she impatiently paced up and down, more full of greed than ever. The instant her ship docked she climbed on board and asked the captain, "What riches did you bring me?"

The wise old captain answered, "My lady, the holds are filled with the staff of life; the finest golden wheat I was able to obtain."

The greedy woman, who had expected gold, silk, ebony, and jade, flew into a rage and screamed, "Over which side did you take it on board?"

Alpine landscape . . . off Enkhuizen. At this stage the future ringdike of the Markerwaard is an island, 3 miles long, crowded with trucks, cranes, an asphalt plant, and offices, not to mention depots of diesel oil and mountains of sand and boulder clay.

The captain told her, "Over the port side, my lady."

"Then take your ship out of the harbor," she said, "and throw the stuff into the sea over the starboard side!"

The captain told her that to do this was wrong and displeasing to the Almighty. He added that no good would come of it and predicted that it might well be her ruin. The lady, now beside herself, took off her costly ring, saying,

"There is as much chance that it will be my ruin as there is that I will ever see this ring again!" With that, she flung her ring into the sea.

The captain took his ship out of port and did as he was ordered to do. A few days later the lady gave a banquet for her friends. The first course was a magnificently prepared fish, which a servant placed next to the lady so she could serve her guests. She cut the fish open and inside lay the glittering ring she had thrown into the sea. After the initial shock everyone laughed and the party continued more gaily than before. Later that evening a courier arrived with the news that one of her ships had been lost in the Baltic. The next day she received word that another had been captured by pirates. And so her ships were lost, one after another, until there were none left. She died in the poorhouse and was buried in Potter's Field.

The *Vrouwezand* outside the harbor is overgrown with tallish, grassy weeds and it is said that these are the offspring of the lady's wheat—

XV

On the night of February 1, 1953, a group of meteorologists and engineers from Waterstaat watched the weather and the unusually high tides with great concern. The winds reached speeds of 100 miles per hour. Many ships off the coast were in distress, and thirty-five, with big freighters among them, were thrown onto the beaches that night. The storm's fury increased and the water rose to the highest recorded levels in history. The Waterstaat people were in constant touch with distant Dike Counts and polder boards, who all kept a worried watch on their dikes.

"Hello, this is BOORSMA near Ouwerkerk, yes, yes, I can hear you. She's still holding but I don't know for how long . . . yes, we've begun alerting the population. . . . I'll keep you posted!"

"Here SCHARENDIJKE . . . there's nothing we can do . . . hopeless . . . the big one will go any moment now. It's already coming over the top!"

"Hello, this is Burgomaster de V. speaking. Things look bad down here. No, sorry, I cannot give you all the information you want; we haven't been able to reach them all . . . electricity is out and the phone lines must be down. . . . No, we tried, there's no way to get through to them . . . yes, I'll do the best I can."

And so the reports came in, bit by bit, from all over Holland. In the early morning the first dikes crumbled. Church bells tolled and sirens wailed their age-old warning: "FLEE, THE WATER IS COMING!"

At first it was not at all clear what had happened; telephone lines were down, electricity out, and most of the Zeeland islands were completely isolated. The first news informing the world of the staggering devastation the storm had wrought came by radio from a Finnish ship that had been thrown onto the beach at Schouwen-Duiveland. Later in the day the magnitude of the disaster became only all too clear: there were sixty-seven tide-carrying breaches in the dikes and hundreds of smaller ones.

Eight per cent of Holland was inundated. The sea had struck so suddenly that many people were drowned in their beds. Others scramble up onto dikes that disintegrated only moments later. People fled into trees, climbing higher and higher as the water lapped at their feet; or onto roofs, clinging to gutters and chimneys—till the house was swept away. Others tried to escape in cars, but the onrushing wall of water overtook and drowned them. Flocks of unsuspecting sheep were swept away into the darkness; tens of thousands of cows drowned in their warm stables. Big, gentle Zeeland horses swam mutely and without understanding around and around in the ice-cold waves. A few fortunate chickens floated away on feed boxes or sat in silent, ruffled terror in swaying trees.

It was a night filled with horror. On Tholen Island a farmer saw his wife and their twelve children drown before his eyes. A couple,

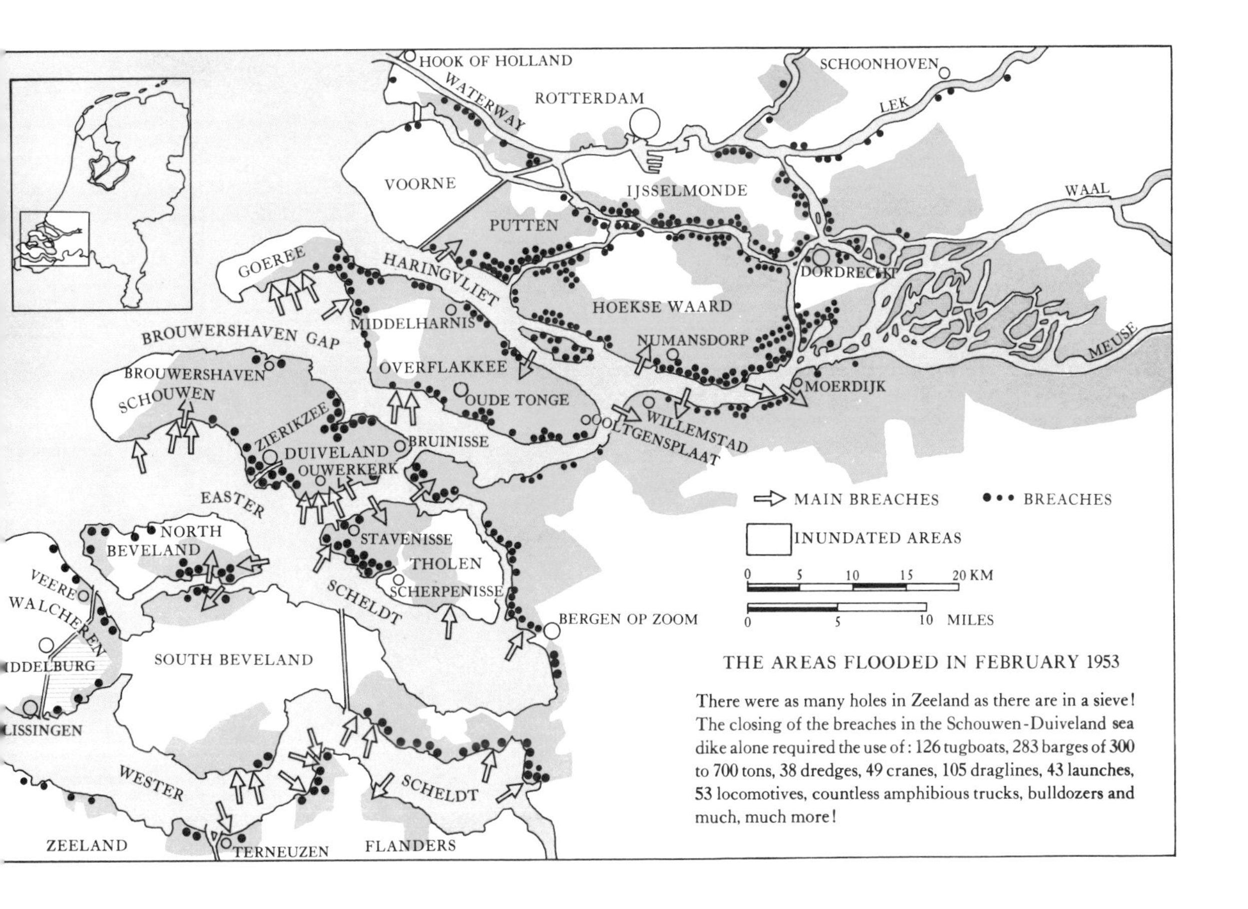

THE AREAS FLOODED IN FEBRUARY 1953

There were as many holes in Zeeland as there are in a sieve! The closing of the breaches in the Schouwen-Duiveland sea dike alone required the use of: 126 tugboats, 283 barges of 300 to 700 tons, 38 dredges, 49 cranes, 105 draglines, 43 launches, 53 locomotives, countless amphibious trucks, bulldozers and much, much more!

surprised by the water, jumped out of bed and raced for the door. The wife got outside, but the husband was caught in the door, slammed shut by the rising water. She fought desperately to free him, but the water kept on rising until she fled and he drowned. A couple was rescued on half the floating roof of their home, their children had been on the other half. On Schouwen a family with eight children was adrift in a small rowboat. After a few hours when the boat overturned the three smallest children were already dead from exposure. Only the father was found the next day clinging to the boat. He had lost his mind.

A night of unspeakable tragedy . . .

The ancient dike peace had not been forgotten and the nation rushed to the rescue. Heroic skippers sacrificed their vessels, sailing them broadside into the dike breaches. The army tried to stop the water with millions of sandbags filled in the bone-chilling cold by elementary-school children. Tens of thousands hurried to the stricken areas; students, doctors, factory hands, and shopkeepers. A strange armada of tugs, fishermen, yachts, and canoes sailed south to the hardest-hit areas from all over the country to take part in the rescue operation.

In some places the impossible was achieved. In Colynsplaat the sea had already smashed the crown of the dike. The water rushed wildly over the top and the dike itself was visibly bulging under the tremendous water pressure when forty men linked their arms, formed a human dike, and temporarily stemmed the flow of water. Then a first-class miracle happened: the waves threw a 100-foot-long barge precisely into the gap and the dike was saved.

Help, too, came from beyond the borders: U. S. Army helicopters arrived from their garrisons in Germany and began taking survivors off roofs and picking them out of trees. Italian troops came halfway across Europe to help. French and Canadian Army engineers came with am-

The mill and the ancient safety mound of Scharendijke. "Yessir! in '53 they plucked us from the cap of the mill. Not a thing to worry about today, though. You can always tell: when the cows graze on the mountain we're in for fair weather!" said the miller-gas station operator.

phibious trucks; Belgians came and British, and Norwegians, and Germans—thousands of them. A compassionate world had come to the rescue.

Inland dikes were strengthened feverishly, for only they now stood between the sea and the heart of Holland. They did hold and finally the storm died down.

But the rescue operation went on. Helicopters skimmed low over the water, from house to house, from tree to tree—like great, loudly humming bees—collecting treasure—human lives!

Then stock was taken: 1835 people drowned, 50,000 farm animals lost, the crops totally destroyed, 47,000 homes and 133 villages and towns under water. Close to half a million acres of farmland taken by the sea.

The Dutch were never a low-spirited lot. "We've still been lucky," they said, "it could have been much worse." And it could have been. If the inland dikes had not held, the sea would have flooded Amsterdam, Rotterdam, and the Hague, and much of the country's industry would have been destroyed. The sea would have torn the heart out of Holland!

It was now February 5. "All dikes must be closed before November when the winter storms will start!" Waterstaat ordered. While the rescue was still in progress, many of the smallest gaps had already been closed by the polder boards and the army. The mighty Luyderzee works were stopped and all their equipment was sent down to Zeeland. But the tide-carrying gaps were—as always—the problem. Each passing tide made them wider and deeper. The one at Ouwerkerk was 650 feet wide, and 50,000,000 cubic yards of water streamed through it four times a day. In September the Ouwerkerk gap was still wide open. Again and again the sea washed the sinker pieces away. Time was running out; the fall storms were on the way.

When the invasion of Normandy was planned in World War II, the allies had built enormous concrete caissons—some with the tonnage of an ocean-going ship—to form the now famous artificial harbors at St. Laurent and Arromanches. A caisson is an oversized concrete floating

The highest levels reached by floods are often marked by special flood-stones such as these, or simply scratched in the bricks with the years and dates added in paint (below).

Bastiaan Kuypers, June 3, 1891, missing. Bastiaan Kuypers, October 11, 1919. Bastiaan Kuypers, May 13, 1952, missing. Johanna Kuypers, January 23, 1923, missing. Grandfather, father, son and mother. Nineteen members of the Kuypers family. Thirty-two de Boers. Twenty-eight Tademas . . . Only their birthdate is given, for the date of death is the same for all: February 1, 1953. The sea still covered the land when Oude Tonge's 300 dead were buried in the only available dry land: the crown of the dike, high above the devastated village.

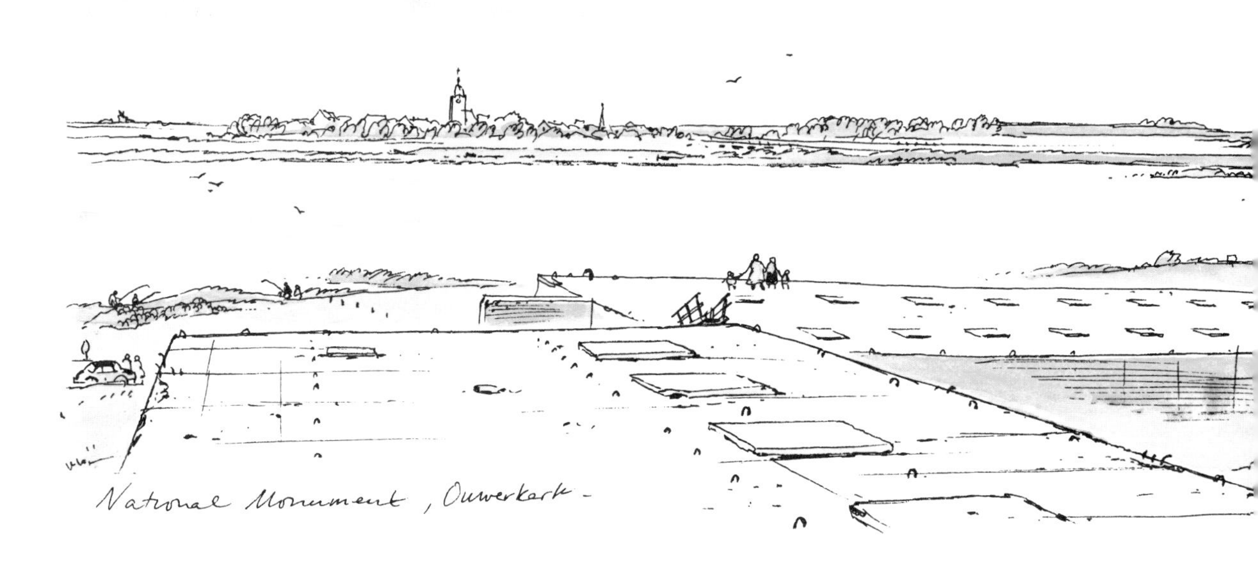

shoe box with valves to let the water enter, so that it can be sunk quickly and exactly where desired. Some had never been used, and these were now towed from England to Zeeland. During the night of November 6, the last of four huge Phoenix caissions was carefully edged into the opening by a fleet of tugboats. The dikes were whole once more! Church bells again rang out over the land, not in warning as they had nine months before, but in exuberant, grateful joy!

Only statistics can give one an idea of what kind of a job it had been. Twelve thousand men labored nine months, using 17,000,000 sandbags, 500 small caissons, and eight big ones. Eighteen million cubic yards of sand and clay were used. Five million square yards of willow and brushwood sinker mattresses were woven by hand—more than 1000 acres!

At year's end the pumping began and slowly the water came down. (The water poured out of Schouwen-Duiveland alone would have been enough to give each of the 3,000,000,000 people on earth a generous bath in a brimming tub!) A ruined land emerged. The canals were filled with sand and mud, as were the houses that were still standing. Big clumps of mussels clung to the trunks of dead trees high above the ground. Everything had to be rebuilt—from farms to roads, from service stations to telephone poles. The soil, so long covered by sea water, had to be carefully nutured back to health with gypsum, chemicals, and fertilizer. The legend of Zeeland's coat of arms reads: *Luctor et Emergo* (Struggle and Rise Again). And this they did.

On the twenty-seventh of August 1963, the great caissons that had closed the dike at Ouwerkerk were declared a national monument. The wartime code name of those caissons was Phoenix, the bird that was consumed by fire and then rose again in youthful vigor from its own ashes.

It turned out to be a prophetic choice.

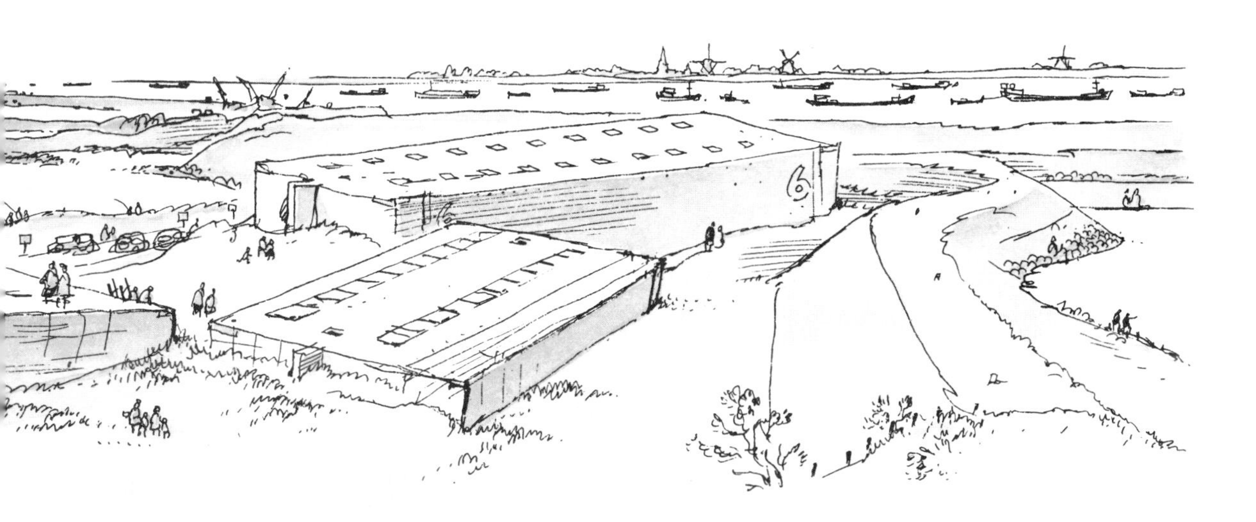

XVI

You can still see windmills everywhere you go in Holland and in a few places you can see a score of them close together. But what has happened to the tens of thousands of windmills that once dotted the land? Where are the mills that dominated the horizon in whatever direction you looked. Where are the mills that were as much a part of any city's skyline as the many church spires?

The last question is easy to answer. Windmills were often constructed on top of city walls or bastions; the additional height helped them to "catch" the wind. A great many mills stood directly outside or close to the city, because the mill's customers lived within the walls and it was an advantage for the manufacturer to be close to the consumer.

Cities also encouraged the building of windmills within the city proper. This made good sense. In times of war, when the city was under siege and cut off from the countryside, wheat could be conveniently ground within the walls. An enormous number of windmills were therefore concentrated in and around cities and towns.

In the early seventeenth century these communities expanded at such a tremendous rate that the city walls were torn down to make room to build and the windmills on the outside, too, were overrun by the growing city. New defensive works were built around the enlarged city, with new windmills sitting on top. New industrial windmills would rise outside the new walls and after a few short years the city would explode again with the same results as before. This process has never ceased and

Amsterdam, Haarlem, Leiden, and Rotterdam are rapidly growing together into one giant community.

It is a sad fact, but the windmill is slowly disappearing. In January 1943 there were 1467 windmills in working condition and 483 in imperfect condition. In 1945, at the end of World War II, there were 1306 mills left undamaged and 473 mills partially destroyed. In 1960 there were 991 windmills left in good condition. Of these, 397 were drainage mills and 594 grinding mills or industrial mills. But, believe it or not, there are still two snuff mills in use. Miners, monks, and the fisherwomen from Scheveningen are the main customers.

Around 1870 miniature windmills appeared here and there on barn roofs. They looked like cute toys, but actually powered circular blades that sawed slats of wood. They were dangerous to work with and many a man lost his fingers in the buzzing blade. Although most people have forgotten why, they're known only as "finger mills" today.

At one time more than 1000 windmills stood close together along the Zaan River, a forest of them! In 1880 there were 288 left; in 1898 174, and today . . . fifteen.

The expanding city was not the mill's only foe. Invading armies always destroyed as many mills as they possibly could, for by destroy-

"De Gooier," last of Amsterdam's city mills. It is a normal windmill set on a brick pedestal in order to catch the wind high above the rooftops.

Amsterdam and its mills in 1600, 1700 and 1800. New mills were built outside the new city walls, but when steam, and later the internal combustion engine, came into general use, torn down windmills were no longer replaced.

ing the windmills they crippled Holland's economy and industry. The Allied air forces bombed German and Japanese factories in World War II for exactly the same reason. Another reason for an enemy to do away with the mills was that the local population could use them as semaphores by the position of the vanes and send messages on enemy troop movements to friendly forces.

World War II took a heavy toll. A mill is often the highest vantage point in the flat land and was often used as an artillery observation post—and then promptly shelled! In the years 1940–45, 132 windmills were destroyed. THE COOLING PIGEON, September '44—blown up; THE GREAT EXPECTATION, April '45—destroyed by retreating Germans; THE GULL, April '45—artillery fire; THE HOPE, May '45—direct hit, burned; 132 windmills, a long casualty list.

But of all the dangers besetting the mill today, fire is the greatest.

Drainage mill & high-rise apartments. Amsterdam.

A windmill is a bone-dry tinderbox covered with thatched reeds. One spark from an overheated axle or a cigarette can set it ablaze. Then there is lightning. Once a fire starts, the mill is consumed in minutes.

This is a typical story of a windmill: in 1687 Willem Pietersz van Ammers received a "windletter" from the town council of Wormerveer, giving him permission to build a sawmill "on the land to the west of the sea dike and bordering on the canal leading to the old lock-gates." The last carpenters left the completed mill on June 6, 1688, and it was handed over to the owner officially in the presence of Simon Hendrickse Honig, agent for the Amsterdam Insurance Company, which issued the fire policy covering THE BLUE EAGLE. Until 1762 THE EAGLE sawed wood for local shipyards. With the decline of shipbuilding in that area, the mill was sold to one Pieter Dirckz and converted into an oil mill. Eighty years later, on October 21, 1841, this advertisement appeared in the local *Waterlandsche Courant:*

"A capital, strong and sturdy oil mill, well kept, with perfect works. Named THE BLUE EAGLE. For sale."

Five days later the mill was sold for 8300 guilders to a group of investors and converted into a paint-color mill. The following January a winter storm severely damaged the mill, which was repaired at considerable expense. The mill changed hands again in 1849, again in 1857. The new owners sold the land on which the mill stood to the factory next door, which was expanding, and moved the disassembled mill to Zaandam, where it was rebuilt and renamed THE RED STAG. From 1867 till 1932 the faithful old mill was worked hard, and at a profit. On

Partially burned mill and the skippers' status-symbol!

This pumping station was built in the early 1900s. The huge boiler room, at a lower level, looks like the stokehold of an early-twentieth-century transatlantic luxury liner. The station is manned by 24 engineers working in three shifts when coal is used (2½ tons per hour!), and by only 11 men when oil is burned. The windmills, whose task was taken over by the station, are kept in perfect working order so they can be used during emergencies.

the night of the twenty-eighth of March 1962, she burned to the ground. "Origin of the fire unknown," said the report of the insurance company.

Improvements and refinements on the windmill never ceased to be discovered. In the drainage mill the screw pump replaced the water wheel and there was a constant—and successful—search for more efficiently shaped vanes for all types of mills. The vanes are not merely great slatted crosses to which the sails are tied, but highly sophisticated aerodynamically designed constructions. The wings of the mill experienced an evolution that can best be compared to that of the airplane. The wings of the earliest mills had as little in common with the last ones built as the wings of Otto Lilienthal's glider with those of the latest jets.

The windmill became the perfect tool, the ultimate generator of economical power—until the engine came along! Steam was the writing on the wall, but the coming of age of the internal combustion engine was the windmill's doom.

Windmills are entirely dependent on the vagaries of wind and a stiff breeze is needed to turn them. In addition, they can not compete with engines in terms of power. Take a polder mill with a wingspread of 100 feet and a water wheel measuring eighteen feet in diameter that lifts the water five feet up. With a fair wind this mill can move 750,000 gallons in twelve hours, and it develops between ten and twenty-five horsepower. The model-T Ford engine of 1910 packing from five to ten h.p. was still no match for the mill, but stronger engines were soon available.

A wheat grinding mill working twenty-four hours a day for one year can produce about 300 tons of flour. A modern factory, on the other

From mill to house – Monnikendam

hand, can grind 2000 tons in twelve hours. At first many millers installed an auxiliary engine in their windmills for becalmed days only, but they began to depend more and more on their reliable power. Once expensive repairs became necessary, the miller often partly dismantled his beloved old mill, removing the wings and the upper works. The price of materials and labor had risen so enormously that he—or the polder board—could no longer afford them. Then the graceful windmill stood sadly at the water's edge; a once proud bird robbed of its wings; an ungainly, purposeless silo. The wrecker usually finished the job after a few years.

The Dutch have founded a "Windmill Preservation Society," which is doing all it can to protect and preserve as many mills as possible. They offer advice on their upkeep and care and purchase historic windmills when one is threatened with extinction. So don't worry—if you ever visit Holland, you will see windmills. Climb the old Kinderdijk near Rotterdam and before your eyes stand nineteen of them close together. You will see them at work, grinding wheat in the south and pumping water wherever there are polders!

The townships of Haarlemmerliede and Spaarnewoude
offer the water windmill THE GULPER for $7.00.
Repairs are urgently needed and will cost $2500.

Whenever an item like this appears in the newspaper (as this one did in 1961), the Society will step in and try to save that rundown mill. As they were 300 years ago, Holland's windmills are once more protected, and exporting them abroad is again strictly forbidden. Fear of economic competition has, of course, nothing to do with it, only the desire to save a small part of an heroic and colorful past—the windmills that kept Holland afloat and in business for so many centuries.

Among the surviving windmill legends, there are many medieval tales of witchcraft and ghosts.

Long ago, so the story goes, a miller was pumping night after night, for the water in his polder had risen because of heavy rains. Each night at the stroke of twelve he was frightened out of his wits by three huge black cats who mysteriously entered his mill. Pious formulas, prayers, and even the Bible he threw at them did not scare them off. One night the miller threw his boiling soup at the cats, which fled the mill screeching terribly.

The next day the miller went to the nearby village and noticed that the first woman he met had her head bandaged; another sat outside her house on a stool and could not walk because she had burned both her legs. Her sister could not milk the cows that day because she had a badly burned hand. The three black cats never bothered the water miller again.

Another miller could not keep his hired hands, for at midnight the mill began to turn by itself and strange and terrifying noises were heard within. One day a fellow came along who had heard of the goings on, but was still willing to give it a try. He did not particularly care to sleep in the mill, but that's where his bunk was, so he had little choice in the matter. At midnight sharp the mill started to turn, even though there was no wind. This hired hand was braver than his predecessors. He stayed and looked through a crack in the wall into the mill proper. Four strange men were seated around a table, feverishly counting heaps of money. They continued counting until the clock struck one. At that moment they disappeared as suddenly as they had come.

The next night the trembling helper and the shaking miller took up position behind the wall and watched it all take place again. When dawn broke they dug under the mill and found a great treasure. The story does not mention how it was divided; in any case, the mill was never bothered by ghosts again.

We are all familiar with the inventive but unconvincing explanations as to "where we came from": "The stork brought you"; "We found you in the cabbage," to mention only two. Along the Zaan River people have for centuries used a quite different story to make it all clear to their inquisitive children: "We went to the water mill at Zaandijk beneath which grows the well-known baby tree. The tree children all called, 'take me, take me!' but we chose YOU."

During the sixteenth century a clever miller saved his city, to which Spanish troops had laid siege for a long time. The population was on the verge of surrendering the city since there was no food left inside. "There is still one pig left," said the miller. "Give it to me and I will

No longer a windmill but still pumping. "I've got 40 electrical horses inside," said the miller of the Katwou polder. "It don't look like much from the outside, but as far as the work goes it sure beats windmilling!"

Old and New power! Leiden.

save us all." They gave it to him with the greatest reluctance. He took it to his mill and tied it to a mill vane. Then he turned the wing cross so that the squealing pig could be seen—and heard—from far away. At the sight of the pig the enemy promptly lifted the siege and left, since there seemed to be plenty of food remaining in the city and they could not expect its imminent surrender.

Old-time millers were well known for their tall tales, like fishermen whose last catch increases in length with each telling. One of the less exaggerated ones was: "We were milling one time and did it ever blow! When we finally wanted to stop the mill that evening to take in the sails, we found the wing cross lying way across the dike. Yessir! That mill had been going at such a clip and there was so much wind that it had kept working all day without the wings! The stones were still spinning like mad, and we ground sixty more bags of flour before the stones even began to slow down. I'll tell you: it was blowing so hard that when you stuck your hand outside, the wind rolled up the skin of your fingers. And that day the potatoes were blown out of the ground!"

Holland, the leaking ship, is still kept afloat only because of the continuous operation of over 2100 pumps. (The many thousands of the smaller pumps are not even included in this number.) They come in all sizes and shapes, from the enormous Diesel-powered pumping stations with the muscle of an ocean liner to the bravely squeaking little ones that keep only one field dry.

Standing on the old curving sea dike, not far from where the straight

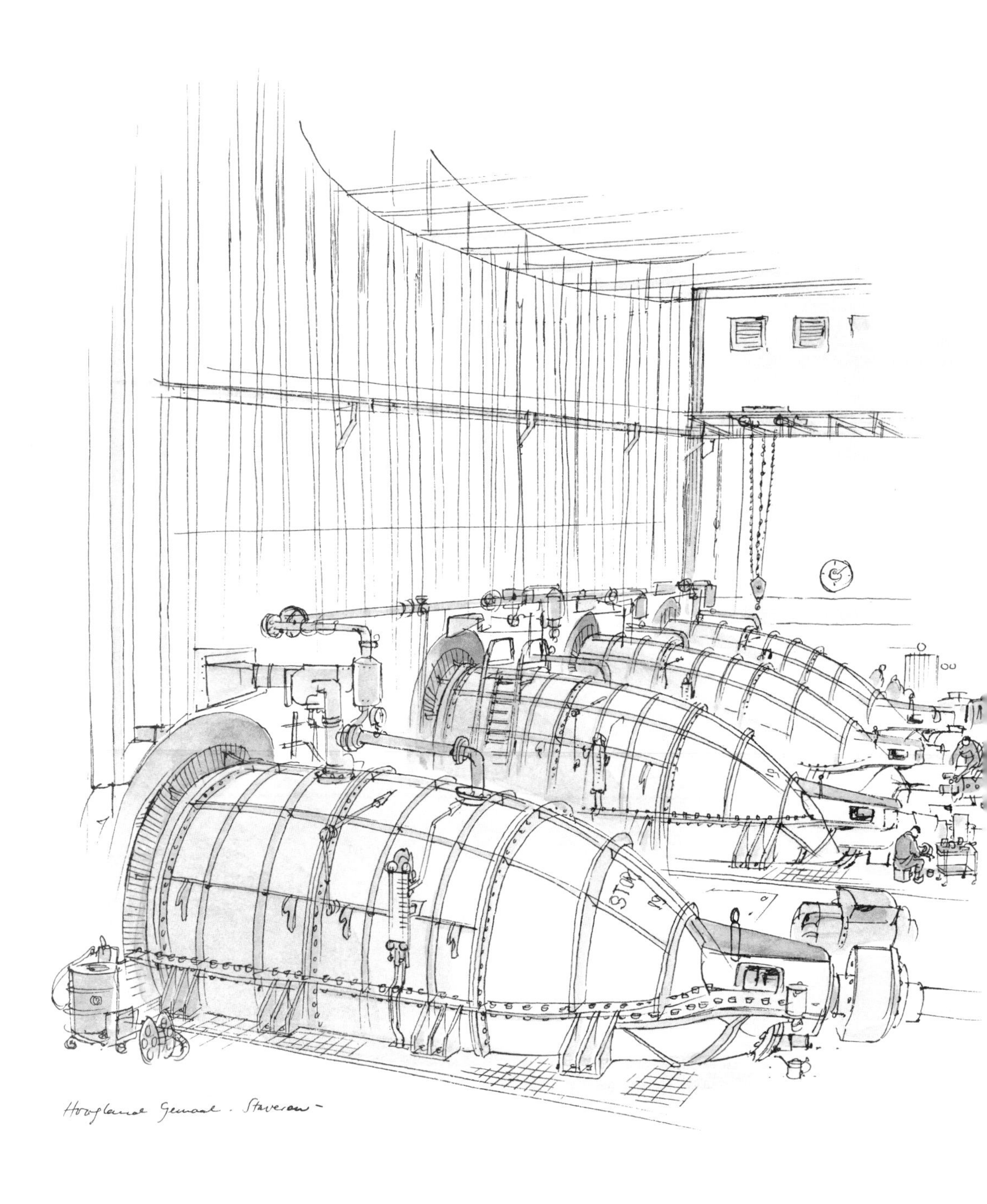

The Hoogland pumping station near Stavoren keeps many of Friesland's basins at the proper level. Its four pumps, each driven by a 570-h.p. electric motor, can throw 180,000 cubic feet per minute into IJssel Lake. From about October 15 to February 15 pumping continues around the clock, seven days a week, without ever stopping, as do the other pumping stations. In addition to the pumps, Friesland's four main sea locks drain 75,600,000 cubic feet of water each 24 hours!

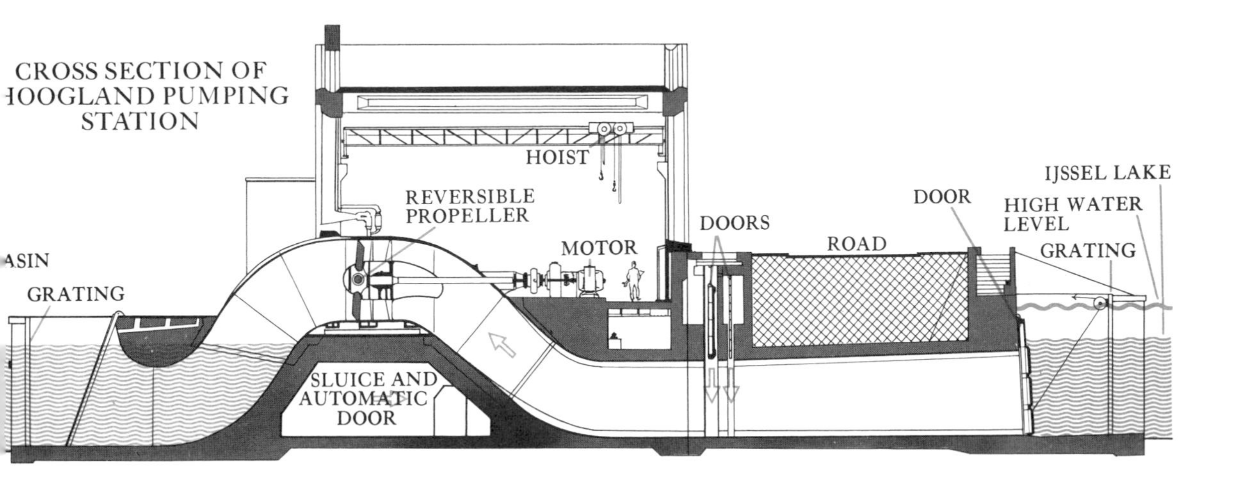

dike of a new Zuiderzee polder branches out of it, you can see a modern pumping station: a factory on the water's edge, clean and efficient. The stark, strong, functional lines that would clash with the gnarled trees and winding roads on the old land go wonderfully well with the new. Its size is in scale with the huge fresh fields: here it belongs!

The interior of the big pumping station is about as romantic as an operating room. Immaculately clean floors—empty factory halls—modernistic mosaics on the walls. The only visible parts of the pumps are the biggest imaginable steel pipes sticking up out of the floor like an armored giant's knees. Below, huge seven-bladed propellers with reversible pitch pump the polder water up at 200 rpm and throw it out into the sea at a clip of 300,000 gallons a minute. (The blades are reversible so they can pump water into the polder during a dry summer.)

When you stand at the base of the three stories tall electro-Diesel engines in the next hall, you might think you are deep down in the engine room of a transatlantic liner. Here are gleaming brass railings and steep steel ladders with brightly shining rungs. In a corner is a machine shop and spare parts for the giants: springs and pistons the size of oil drums. The pumps are run by the huge, humming electric motors. The Diesels are here for safety—they will generate electricity if the regular source should fail.

The twentieth-century water miller wears a business suit and sits behind a steel desk in a quiet office. Framed polder maps hang on the pastel-colored walls. From here he controls his "mill" with a few push-buttons and a series of dials.

Out of one picture window you look onto the sea. Out of the opposite window you can see the treeless land, flat as a table top, lush meadows cut by hundreds of canals and ditches. The widely spaced farms sit like miniature pieces on a gigantic chessboard, not friendly, not unfriendly, just big and fertile.

But off to the side, half hidden behind the twisting dike, is the warm old land. Tile roofs peek from between the full trees at the tall sky. Villages are close together and the horizon is dotted with small towns and graceful bell towers. This is "home." Close by on a low dike an old polder windmill is busily at work. Seen from the window it looks small, almost like a toy, but when you walk down the path alongside the canal leading to the mill, it seems to grow larger and larger. And once you stand in front of it you see that the tips of the flailing arms reach 120 feet into the sky. You hear the wind and the swoosh! swoosh! swoosh! each time the great arms tumble by, the splashing of water down below, and creaking way up in the top. Reddish-tanned sails are set upon the latticework of the wings. The dark brown octagonal hide of the mill is made of closely shorn weathered thatch. Here and there small windows—like inquisitive little eyes—look out from between the stubble.

The base of the mill is a house—old pink bricks, red geraniums, and glass curtains behind the cozy windows. Over the Dutch doors, painted bright green, is the old gilded carving: DE WATERDIEF—Anno. 1723,

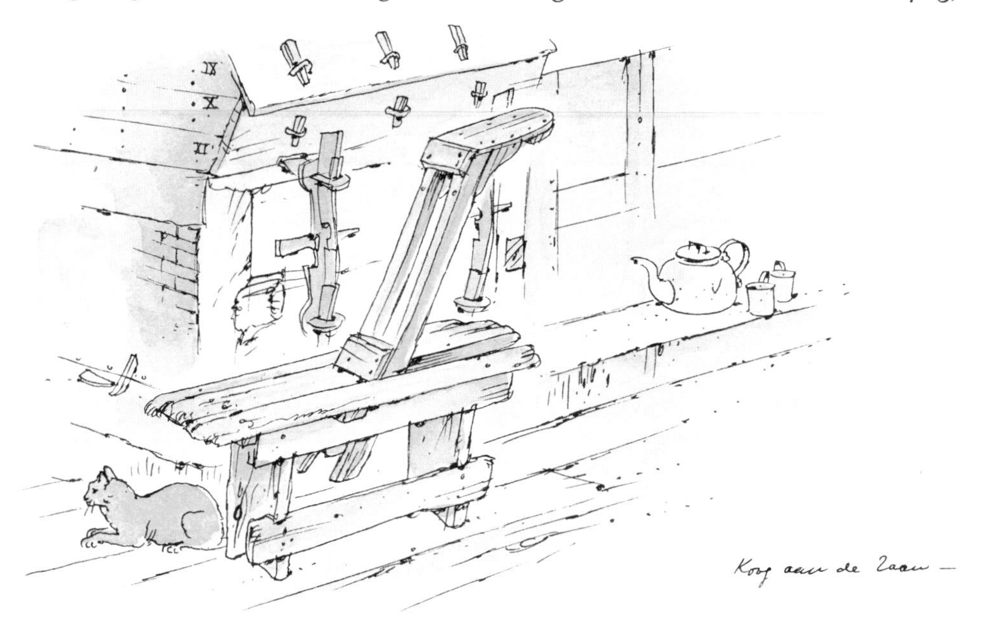

There was never a windmill without its miller's shaving bench. When the mill was working the busy miller simply could not afford to take time out for shaving. It was during those periods of high water in polder country, or after the harvest when grinding mills worked ceaselessly, that the local barber armed with his brushes, straps and straight razors made the rounds from mill to mill.

One that's been saved! The corn mill of Krabbendijke in Zeeland is stripped completely, then carefully rebuilt with as many of the old parts as possible. "He'll be better than new," said the grimy millwright. "Come back in six months and you won't know him!"

THE WATERTHIEF. Around the brickwork runs a broad painted stripe, freshly whitewashed—for better visibility when the mill is worked at night.

The Dutch doors open and the friendly miller's fat wife slips into her wooden shoes, which are parked outside. "Yes, Meneer', I saw you already coming along the dike." The flat land does not hide anything. "I said to myself, d'you think he's coming our way? We're not used to seeing many strangers here, you know. . . . You from Waterstaat? Come on in, the boss will be back in a minute."

Inside it is just as cozy as you expected. The woodwork is painted a vivid blue; your reflection in the brass bowl of the kerosene lamp is grotesquely distorted. On the cupboard stand old vases; a gay tablecloth is on the table. There are a few old easy chairs, a photograph of the queen, and, hanging on the wall, some Victorian oleographs. On the stove simmers something that smells awfully good. A radio plays a happy tune. The miller's wife beams with pride: "Yes, sir, we were connected with the electricity last spring!"

Outside the window the mighty vanes sweep steadily by, darkening the room for a second each time they pass, like the shutter in a camera, and then the sunlight streams in again.

"We've had some wet days," says she, "been milling solidly."

On the brick walk there is the cloppity-clop of wooden shoes. "There's the boss now!" The old miller comes in on his stocking feet (wooden shoes are always left outside; upside down when it rains!).

"You from Waterstaat?" asks the miller, too, but his wife answers,

You often find one or more small models of the big mill standing close to it or on display in the miller's geranium bed. These toy mills are made by the miller when there is no work to be done.

"No, he isn't, but he'd like to see the mill and do some sketching."

The miller nods thoughtfully, then pulls out a big old-fashioned watch on a long chain. "Come at the right time, have to go upstairs anyway." You follow your host up a narrow flight of stairs into the dark, empty belly of the mill.

After your eyes have become used to the dark, you see the mighty oak timbers that form the frame of the mill, skillfully fitted together, secured with heavy pegs. In the center turns the axle. Through the cobwebbed little windows beams of sunlight stab into the dark. Up and up you go, patting the two-feet-square crossbeams once in a while just for the feel of it. "Aye," the miller says from above, "the old THIEF is still as sound as the day on which she was built!"

Through the center of the mill turns the main shaft, driven by the vanes. After what seems an endless climb, you are in the top, here the axle enters the mill. "Got to keep 'er greased . . . five times a day. Yes, sir! Wouldn't say that I'm almost seventy-one, would you now? . . . yes, sir! seventy-one next September. Been here going on forty-eight years!"

The turning shaft is carefully lubricated with something white. ". . . best lard you can get. Use seventeen pounds of it a day!"

Behind you, turn the gears. The hundreds of wooden pegs tumble playfully together, without missing once. Noisily but smoothly the ancient wooden fingers interlock incessantly. Through the cracks the wind blows in your face. "That's it," says the miller, "let's go down, but be careful!"

You blink your eyes, blinded for a moment, when you step outside into the breezy summer day and smell freshly mown grass. Where the canal, which is connected with the main waterways in the polder, enters the mill a vertical wooden grating keeps floating vegetation and debris from entering the wheelhouse. Bolted to it is a tall white gauge with many black marks: the Amsterdam scale. "Can't see it now, but underwater there's the mark. Got to keep pumping till that's out of the water. Two more days—if it doesn't rain."

The water enters the mill through a twenty-foot-long brick tunnel—the tailgate—at the end of which turns the big scooped wheel (others of more recent date have a screwpump). This wheel lifts the water eight feet up and dumps it into the canal on the other side of the mill; where it leaves the mill the water foams and froths—a king-sized milkshake.

"I'll show you the wheel," says your host, "but stand back or you'll get soaked!"

Two slanting doors in the side of the mill are opened; a spray of water flies about. Inside the water splashes so violently that you cannot see the wheel.

"Too bad," says the miller, "but she's pumping mightily!"

On the other side of the wheel are two doors that open when the water is thrown out of the polder and are closed by the pressure of the higher canal water when the wheel stops, keeping water of higher levels from entering the polder: the sluice gate of old.

Most polder waters abound in eel, a fish that likes to swim with the

Zaande Schans: Windmill Country! The entrance to a parkinglot.

waterflow. So when the mill is pumping, great quantities of eel swim into the tailgate. "Fishing's my sideline," explains the miller happily. "I hang the net in the tailgate and the eel swim into it. It's doing it the easy way. You a fisherman? Come back this fall and we'll get some pike, that's real fishing!!"

When the water has risen above the LEVEL mark on the big gauge and pumping must begin, the miller climbs into the latticework of the vanes and—like a sailor—makes sail. If the wind is very strong he can put a reef in the vanes, again as on a sailboat. Then the top of the mill, to which the millcross is attached, has to be turned so that it faces the wind. From the cap protrude horizontal beams, the ends of which are connected with vertical beams that meet near the ground. Here an enormous wheel is mounted. Wrapped around the spindle of the wheel is a chain which is connected to a heavy post. There are twelve of these posts spaced around the mill: the chainposts. By turning the great wheel the chain is shortened and the heavy milltop is slowly turned around. When the chain is wound completely around the spindle, the miller unwraps and attaches it to the next post, repeating the process until the mill is in position. It is hard work.

From the back of the top there protrudes a long gaff with a rope hanging down from it. "That's the brake," says the miller. "You slowly release it and the vanes begin to turn. You stop it the same way, but

Zaanse Schans

Said the water miller from the Assendelft polder: "Ja, mijnheer, the soil here is shrinking and we have to pump much harder than a few years back. Oh yes, I can get away all right, but I must grease the motors every two days. Waterstaat gave me a new one and I have two of them now. In the old days I took off on my bike, but now I've got a little car. Lucky they took out the old 1877 steam engine, for the car fits nicely in the boiler room. I'm sort of tired right now. Been pumping five days in a row. You know, mijnheer, physically it's not exhausting, but if you get what I mean, mentally it's a bit monotonous . . ."

carefully! It's a tricky job, yessir, it is. If you don't watch out you can wreck a mill in no time—and I have never run a mill to pieces!

"Some twenty-two—no, let me see . . . twenty-three years ago the old vanes were replaced; these are the new kind, streamlined . . . good thing, too. Get twenty per cent more work out of her now."

The miller beams, "Gonna be clear tomorrow." A good miller is a weather expert: he watches the sky all his life, for a sudden squall or a storm catching the mill unprepared, or with too much sail set, can break it. When it begins to blow hard, the miller will watch the other mills in the distance to see whether they find it necessary to reef, just as a sailor in a race watches the sails of the others. The wear on the sails is considerable and, therefore, each mill has two suits of them.

In times of drought there are weeks that the miller is idle. He gets a normal night's sleep and makes small repairs, mends the sails and keeps his mill well painted. But when it rains a lot—and that it does in Holland!—the miller cannot turn in for nights on end. For when the mill works it has to be watched and tended like a newborn baby. "Shortening sail on a pitch dark night isn't easy . . . especially in winter . . . a few years ago we pumped for three weeks solid, the wife took over while I slept. That was a bitter winter . . . had to take the sails down one night—there was a gale blowing—but everything had frozen stiff. I says to myself, this doesn't look good, Hendrik, you better do something about it. So I got an ax and the wife and I chopped those sails down." He fills his pipe thoughtfully. "You said you wanted to do some sketching . . . I've got some things to do myself; the polder board is coming tomorrow . . . THE THIEF better look shipshape . . . they might give me a raise!"

It is strictly forbidden for water millers to go to bed at night when the mill is working. When, in days gone by, the wind died down at night and the mill stopped, the miller could turn in, but only after having tied a wooden shoe or other heavy object to a wing tip. When the wind freshened again, the banging of the object on the side of the mill or on the walk would waken the miller right away.

In polders worked by a number of mills, the millers took turns waking each other. But millers in isolated areas sometimes went to sleep rolled up in a blanket tied with a rope to a vane, when the wind had died. When it began to blow once more, the miller would be flung out of the blanket rather urgently.

The polder below lies in peaceful rest. A blue egret rises on lazy wings, a kicking frog in its beak, and disappears behind the reeds. The miller's fat dog has curled up on the warm red bricks in the sun, between the wooden shoes. Behind the green doors water loudly splashes and the wind sings past the flailing wings. These are the only sounds.

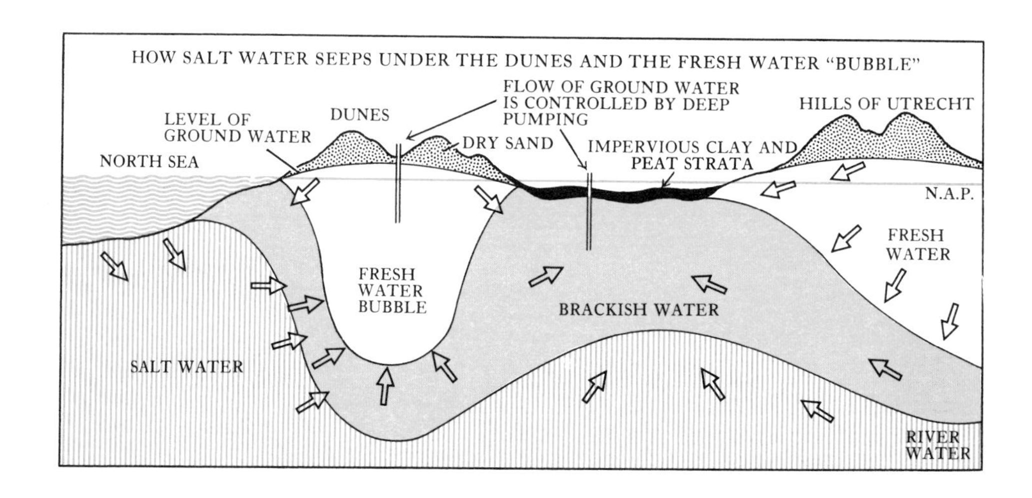

XVII

The pollution of its rivers and coastal waters is one of the universal problems faced by almost every highly industrialized nation on earth, and Holland is no exception.

The Dutch have to defend themselves especially against this danger—and danger is the word!—for if they were to do nothing about it, Holland's soil would inevitably become infertile in but a few centuries. Holland would become a land where, quite literally, not a leaf of grass could grow.

Worse, the pollution problems are compounded by the fact that the sea has been attacking in a new way: salt is slowly creeping in under the dikes. Salt enters the country by way of the rivers with each incoming tide, and through Rotterdam's enormous harbor complexes. It sneaks in through sluices and lockgates—every time the great locks at IJmuiden are used to let a ship in or out of Amsterdam harbor, 3000 tons of pure salt enter the country. And the locks are in constant use.

Salt has always been prevented from seeping in underneath the dunes by the big "bubble" of fresh water that hangs under them. This is rain water that has filtered through the dunes, and this great reservoir of pure fresh water supplies most of the water needs of western Holland, where its consumption for private use and industry has increased tremendously. At one time the increased tapping of this invisible barrier against the salt had shrunk it so much that it no longer acted as a shield against the salt. More was being taken out than Nature put back in. This problem was solved by constructing a pipe system through which river water is pumped into the dunes, and the "bubble" can now be controlled.

The salinity in Holland had always been counteracted by the rain and by the rivers, which washed the incoming salt back to sea again. But the rivers themselves have become polluted and once abundant salmon and sturgeon disappeared from these waters years ago. The Rhine is today a scenic sewer through which salt from German mines, chemicals and waste from the Ruhr and from France flow down to the sea. This pollution seeps in under the river dikes as well, putting a most unpleasant squeeze on the Dutch.

Engineers are experimenting with various methods of reducing the salt inflow in rivers and harbors. By one of these methods, powerful compressors create an "air screen" of fine bubbles across a harbor entrance. It has been found that these walls of air can keep out better than fifty-five per cent of the salt when the tide comes in, and slow down silting as well.

Zeeland has always been especially vulnerable and new plans to improve the situation there are constantly drawn up. There have been two island plans, three island plans, flood barrier plans, and single dike

Pollution of air and water: the great oil refineries near Rotterdam.

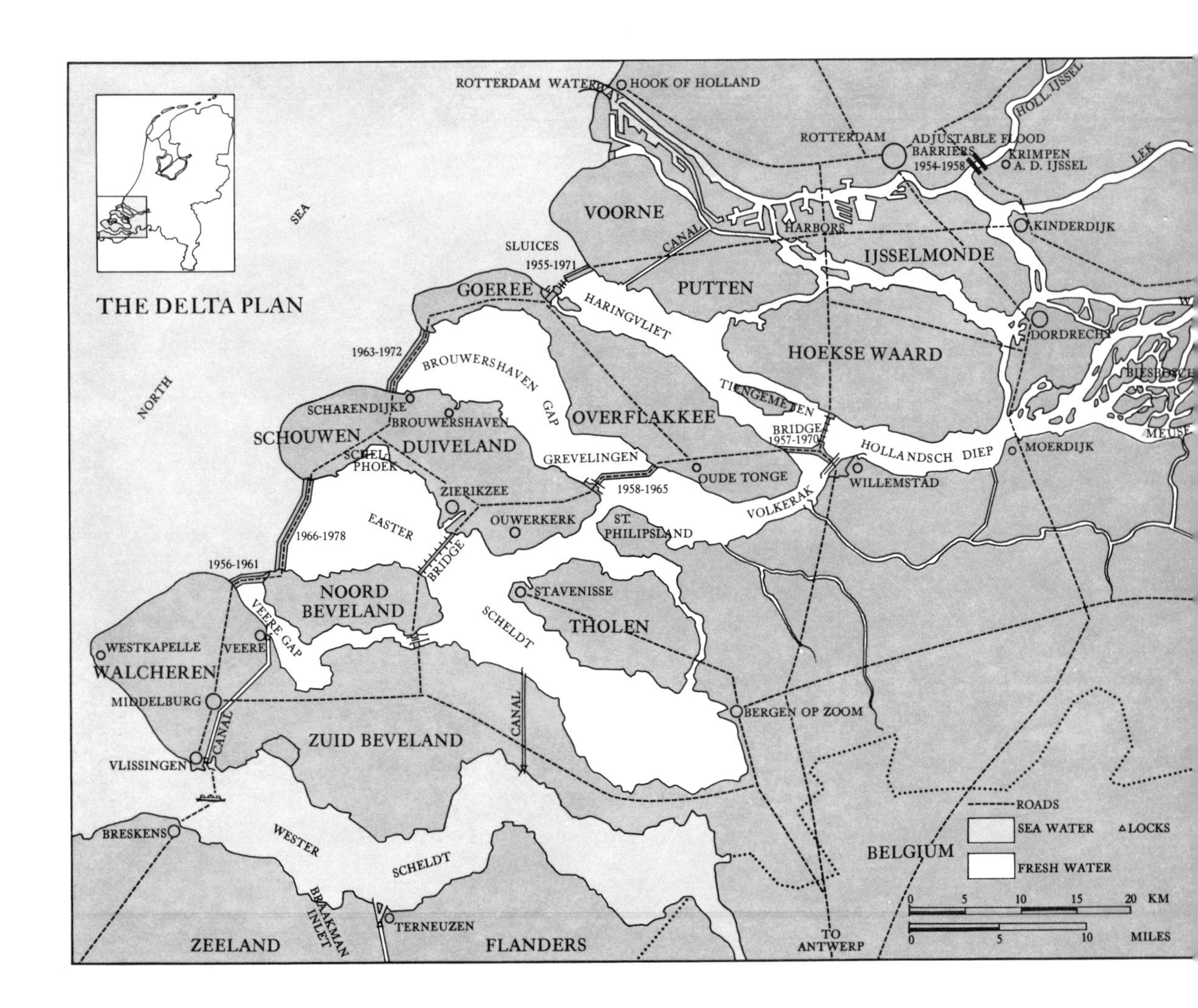

plans; dusty stacks of them. But it was easier said than done: the waters around the islands are deep and treacherous, the currents unusually strong and swift. (The Zeelander differs physically from the rest of the Dutch population because these waters isolated the islands for centuries. Their ancient island race is still preserved; they are short and have dark eyes and hair.) Also it was impossible to close off the inlets because the rivers flow through them to sea. This was a tough nut to crack!

The "Delta Plan"—visualized by Vierlingh four centuries ago—was proposed in its present form in 1949. It involved an ingenious combination of dikes, sluices, and movable river barriers. In 1950 the Meuse was dammed off at the sea and this was the first step toward an ambitious and distant goal: the diking in of Zeeland as a whole. The Waterstaat people had not forgotten the D-Day caissons that had been salvaged and had saved the day for Walcheren in 1945, and in 1952 they began building their own.

The standard caisson is enormously tricky to handle and timing is of the ultimate importance when closing tidal gaps. In 1922 a Waterstaat engineer had an ingenious idea: a free-flow caisson, the "culvert caisson." He knew that an undisturbed tidal flow is absolutely essential and that the slightest change made in the tide's natural pattern would inevitably result in the destruction of the islands, so he designed a caisson with two levels. The bottom level is open on the two long sides, but steel doors can be dropped to close the openings. The top level is like an empty box. Wooden walls are temporarily attached to its open sides and the caisson floats. The caisson is towed to the spot where it is to be used and the wood is taken away. The concrete caisson sinks like a stone, its top level well above high tide. The top half is quickly pumped full of sand and weighs the caisson down firmly. Then the next one is rammed tightly against it, and so on. The caissons thus form a sea wall through which the tides flow freely and harmlessly.

At the moment when the ebb is at its lowest, just before it again begins to rise, the tide is "dead." For a short time all water movement ceases, and this is when all the steel doors are slammed shut. In a few seconds the open bridge becomes a solid, watertight wall and the sea is locked out forever. Then sand and clay are heaped over the steel and concrete wall, and it is faced with stone. In time it will look the way a self-respecting dike should!

Thirty years after their conception, Waterstaat began building the caissons. Later, refinements were added, such as extra concrete "boxes" on top. This meant that the culvert caissons could be used in much deeper water.

Zeeland-Flanders was once almost cut in half by the Braakman Inlet. Here two old Phoenix caissons—altered into free-flow caissons—were used

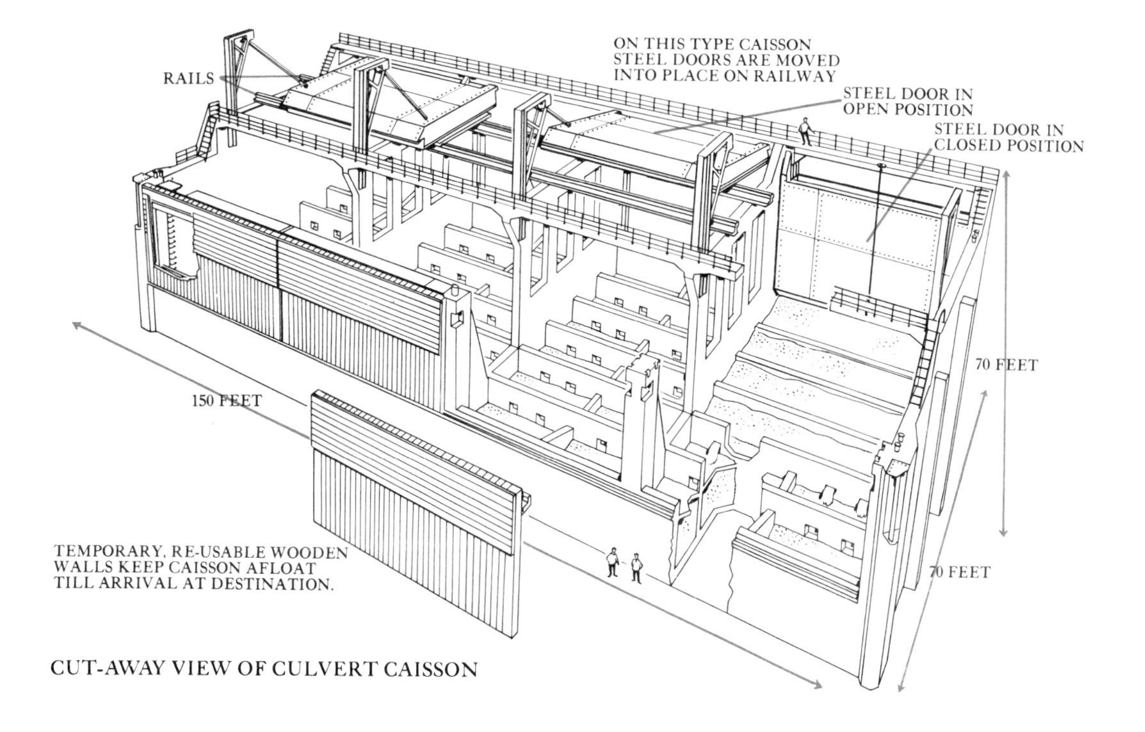

CUT-AWAY VIEW OF CULVERT CAISSON

One reason why the old dikes cannot be heightened: from the earliest days people lived safely on the dikes, and these small communities evolved into towns and villages, like Tienhoven on the Lek River. By raising these dikes thriving communities would have to be destroyed, not to mention the irreparable loss of countless cultural and historical monuments.

for the first time. They worked like a charm. The land gained was only 3200 acres, but the inlet had been a tough one (it was one and a half miles wide, forty feet deep, and the difference between high and low tide was sixteen feet). The experience gained was invaluable.

By now you know that the Dutch are fond of commissions and have a remarkable knack for making them work. A new commission had been working on plans to dam the Easter Scheldt. Their report was delivered in January 1953, and the ink was not quite dry when the sea struck. Three weeks after the catastrophe a "Delta Commission" was formed. Nature had once again forced the Dutch into a gigantic undertaking. The preliminary plans were completed in 1954 and the plan became law in November 1957. The plan, in short, called for the construction of four mighty dikes connecting Zeeland's islands to South Holland, shrinking the coastline to barely 300 miles. A series of secondary dikes and locks and sluice complexes, and river flood barrages were also to be built. The mouth of the Scheldt River was to be left open because it is the entrance to the great port of Antwerp.

Why this enormous undertaking? Because there was no choice. With Holland slowly sinking and the level of the sea rising, Zeeland is es-

Whenever a dike is cut or lowered by even a few inches over a width of only three feet, provisions must be made to fill the opening at a moment's notice. The sea dike in Den Oever on Wieringen (top left) had to be cut to let trucks reach the harbor filled with fishing trawlers in order to load the catch. Two heavy doors can be closed to lock out the rising sea. Two walls of wooden beams are dropped into the slots of the 18th-century river gate at Wijk bij Duurstede (bottom left), and the space between them

packed with straw and manure when the Lek River rises in the spring. A secondary road cuts through a dike, miles away from the sea (top right). Here, too, wooden beams, neatly stacked and carefully protected from the elements by a roof, are placed in the slots when danger threatens. A single concrete block can be put across the bicycle path crossing a river dike (center right), and those few inches could spell the difference! The highway Utrecht-s'Hertogenbosch has a barrier of steel doors to close the dike.

pecially threatened. Its 700 miles of dikes are older and smaller than those in the North. Engineers found that it was possible to heighten Zeeland's dikes a maximum two or three feet. They could not be built higher because the soil below, and the old dikes themselves, would crumble under the extra weight. Thus, heightening the new dikes would be only a very temporary solution.

Another plan had been suggested at one time: pump sand and clay out of the North Sea into the low parts of Holland and build them up to a height of 100 feet. This was, of course, unthinkable, since it would turn most of Holland into one large Pompeii. It might be said of this plan, "The operation was a great success but the patient died."

The Delta Plan was obviously the last solution. After the completion of the dams, the new "Lakes" would not be reclaimed, but would remain fresh-water basins—buffers against salinity. The canalization of the rivers with huge storm gates that could be lifted up or let down would also aid in the fight against the incoming salt. In addition, these gates

The weir at Hagestein in the Lek River, one of three, is closed 3 months in an average year, and partly closed for another 6 months to keep the river navigable. Ships then must pass through the lock. The Rhine supplies enough water during the other 3 months to leave the "visors" raised.

would allow the Dutch to direct Rhine water wherever it might be needed; in summer to the IJssel River—or to any other river—to improve navigation; to the IJssel Lake in order to help maintain the correct level, or through the new Zeeland lakes to flush away the salt whenever required. There would be other side benefits. The new dikes would end the island's ancient isolation and highways across the dikes would be an economic boon to the province. The new lakes would be outstanding recreational areas for crowded Holland and would offer some of the finest sailing and best fresh-water beaches in Europe. However, the owners of the renowned Zeeland oyster industry and the mussel fishermen were not happy about the Delta Plan for it meant the end of their prospering businesses.

NOORDZEE
VLIETEPOLDER
VEERSE GAT
West

The technical and mathematical problems that had to be solved stagger the imagination. Special tidal and sea-current computers were built and, with their aid, formulas were worked out in about three years, which would have taken mathematicians without computers twenty-five years to complete.

In Delft's hydrological laboratories acres and acres of scale models of the estuary were constructed for studies and experiments. Some of these models were made of special materials that crumbled under pressure exactly as a real dike or island would. The million-dollar question was, "How high must we build the new dikes?"

A "Stormflood Commission" which had met in 1939 abandoned the old rule of thumb that determined the required height and strength of new dikes and dams. The old system was based mainly on the levels reached by the sea during past stormfloods. The new system is based on the laws of probability. To arrive at these new formulas scientists, of course, used measurements from the past, but they now headed directly to the source: to those forces which create the conditions that place Holland in such mortal peril time and time again. Waterstaat's engineers and meteorologists had already been working on these formulas for fifteen years, basing their calculations on what the situation would be in the year 2000.

Every hydraulic possibility and its side effects had to be taken into consideration. Lely, for example, had correctly predicted that building the enclosing dike would raise storm flood levels along the Frisian coast by more than three feet. The simplest explanation of the technical,

In 1947 Waterstaat ordered this scale model of Zeeland; the big rivers extending as far upstream as the tidal effects are visible. One step takes you across Veere Gap, and a wooden bridge leads from North Beveland to Schouwen. The ebb tide moves rapidly out to sea, creating ripples and eddies between the concrete shores and shallows. A minute later the tidal gullies are emptied. Only water from the rivers winds its way through the slippery, algaed maze to the "sea." Then the full-throated sound of the centrifugal pump starts up and the tide rushes in again. The air is hot and moist, like in a green house for tropical plants. Thousands of copper rods embedded in the model duplicate the natural resistance the waterflow encounters. Small floats connected with hair wires to delicate recorders, whose needles are quivering nervously on graph paper, measure the rise, fall and speed of the water with incredible accuracy. Bells ring, gears suddenly crank up a gate marked HARINGVLIET and a torrent of water bursts inland. Stilt-legged motors madly spin white rods, which simulate the effect the rotation of the earth has on the currents. Lights blink and the tidal clock moves through the next 12 hours in 2½ minutes. A new gigantic model of the Easter Scheldt has been built in the North East Polder. To solve the problems connected with the closing of the Haringvliet alone, 5 models of the dam and the installations had to be constructed. Also: 1 model to study wave diffraction; 4 models to study wave attacks on sluice gates; 3 models to study scouring and bed protection and 1 model to study navigation. The same had to be done for most of the other delta dams!

"My job is almost done," said the young engineer in the caisson building pit near Willemstad, 35 feet below high tide. "The last of the wooden walls are going in place today." These culvert caissons with the displacement of a destroyer escort, are 150′ long, 50′ wide and 70′ high: the size of a 7-story apartment house. The wedge-shaped piece to the left is tailor-made to fit the shore. "The pumps that kept the pit dry will stop tomorrow and ground water will slowly rise. A small boat is already inside, to get

to and from the caissons." In May 1969 a dredge will have chewed through the ring-dike and cut a hole big enough to tow the caissons out into the Volkerak, where a huge sill has been prepared to receive them. They will be placed as closely together as possible, then steel nets will be hung in the gaps and filled with stones. At the same time 4000 cubic yards of sand will be pumped into the ballast box to keep them firmly in place.

After a disastrous flood in 1808 it was decided to dam the Hollandse IJssel on this spot. Nothing ever came of it. In 1860, after another calamity, a wooden barrier and a lock were built but did not last. These adjustable flood barrages at Krimpen aan den IJssel were completed in 1958, and now the Dutch can bolt their front door securely when the water rises. The advantage is twofold: dikes and polders behind the closed barrage are safe, and salt cannot enter the country beyond the lowered doors.

mathematical, and meteorological reasoning behind the Delta Project would fill a book several times the size of this one.

The highest level reached by the sea in February 1953 was twelve feet six inches above N.A.P. and this was the highest level on record. The scientists concluded that storm levels of up to sixteen feet five inches above N.A.P. could occur. This was unlikely, but it was possible. The chances are that this would happen only once in 10,000 years.

Waterstaat decided that this was an acceptable risk, and the height of the Delta dikes is based on a "once-in-10,000-year" calculation. The crown of the dike between Walcheren and North Beveland is forty-four feet above N.A.P. It sounds pretty reassuring, but should the seemingly impossible ever happen, the existing dikes will be there as a second line of defense.

Three years before the Delta Plan became law, the actual construction work on the river stormflood barrages had begun in the Hollandse Ijssel.

A concrete wall raised the crown of an inland dike near Scherpenisse some three feet. The same is done throughout Zeeland with sea dikes as well. Many different systems to protect dike slopes have been developed. (Below) Here are just a few of them.

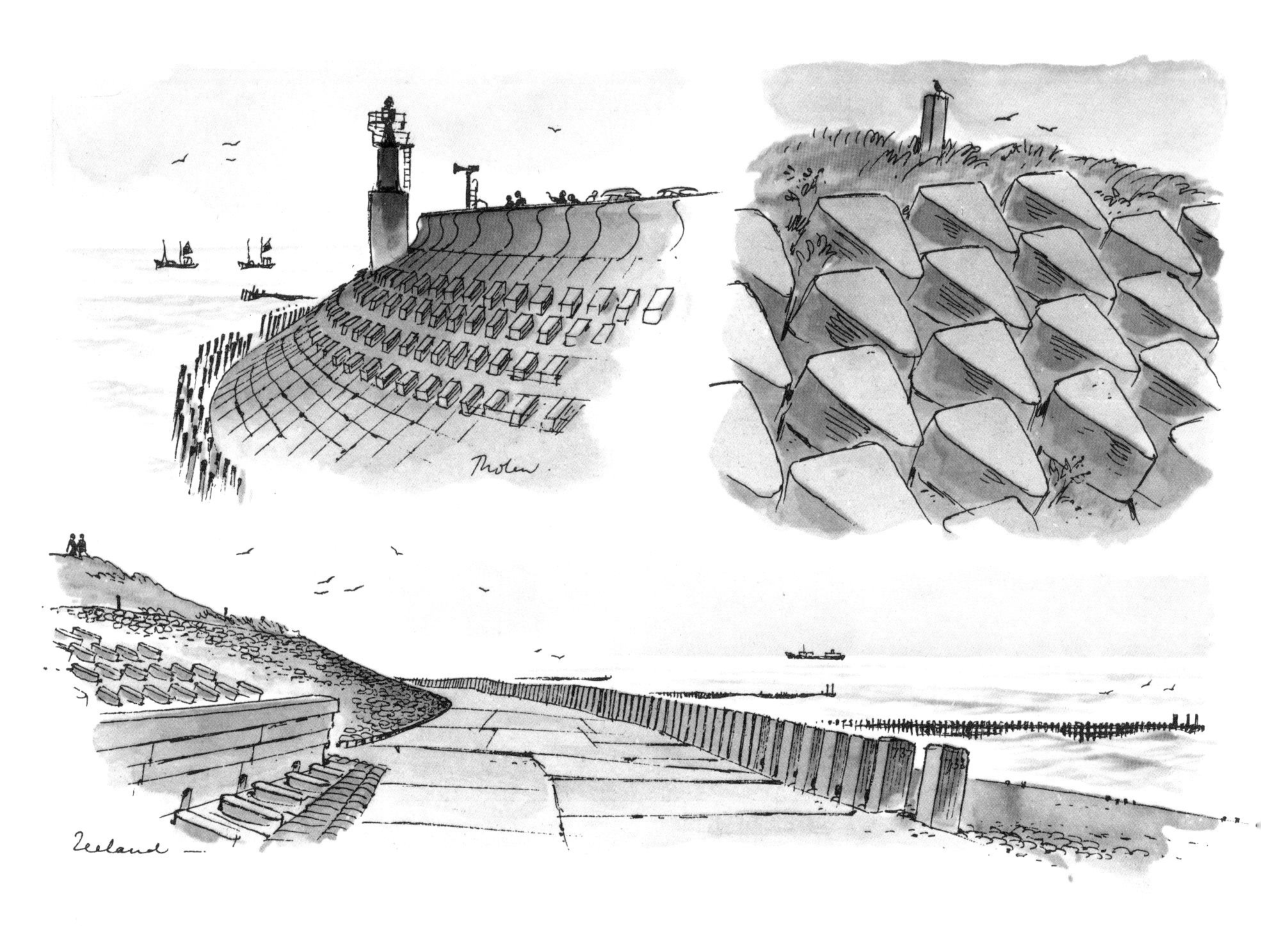

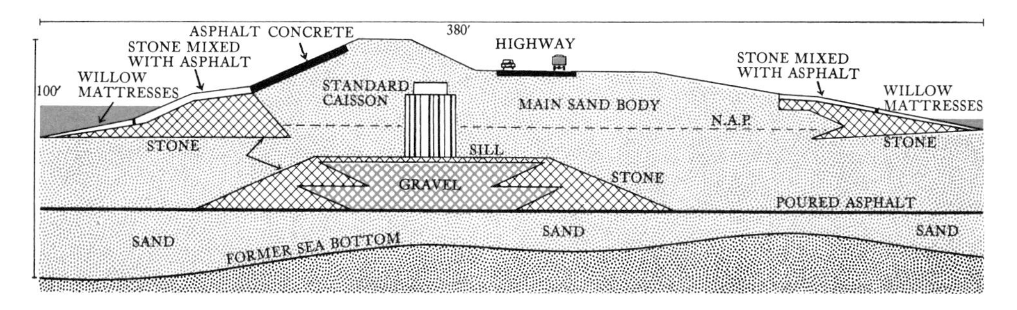

Section of a finished delta dike, showing a caisson resting on the sill, which was prepared years before the caissons were actually placed.

A host of new methods and materials have been developed for the Delta Project and used with great success. Masters Vierlingh and Leeghwater would have been goggle-eyed at the asphalt, plastic sheeting, and nylon used to build new dikes. The hair of those two old master dikers would stand on end if they could see the caissons that are buried within the new dikes. They would most vehemently argue: "A dike should never, but NEVER, contain foreign bodies!"

Holland does not grow enough brushwood and willows to supply the vast quantities needed to weave the sinker pieces used in Zeeland, and for that reason nylon is being used now. This must have been a most unpleasant discovery for our old friend the pile worm and his distant cousin the *Teredo,* or shipworm, who had jointly begun to eat their way into the proceedings.

The reed dike of old has become a far less romantic asphalt dike. A special machine was designed to coat the dike—from deep below the surface of the water to well above flood level—with a heavy layer of special asphalt. Other dikes are protected by concrete belts that look like the treads of monstrous snow tires or like the dragon-toothed tank traps of the Siegfried Line. Salt seepage is fought with a new "deep-pumping" method, whereby the deepest strata are pumped empty before their contents can rise or penetrate inland.

This strange floating factory coats the sea bottom with thick, 17-foot-wide ribbons of sand-asphalt. In the future it may be unnecessary to sink huge hand-woven willow mattresses for the foundations.

Wherever dike projects are under way you will come upon carefully stacked, massive amounts of willow and brushwood from which the mattresses are woven.

In a work harbor, a huge mattress is woven on a black-top slope and launched mechanically, inch by inch, as it comes out of the "loom." Once it is afloat more garlands of bundled wood are added and hammered in place with wooden stakes or tied down with heavy twine. Then tugs will move the mattress over its final resting place, where it is quickly sunk with stones when the tide is turning.

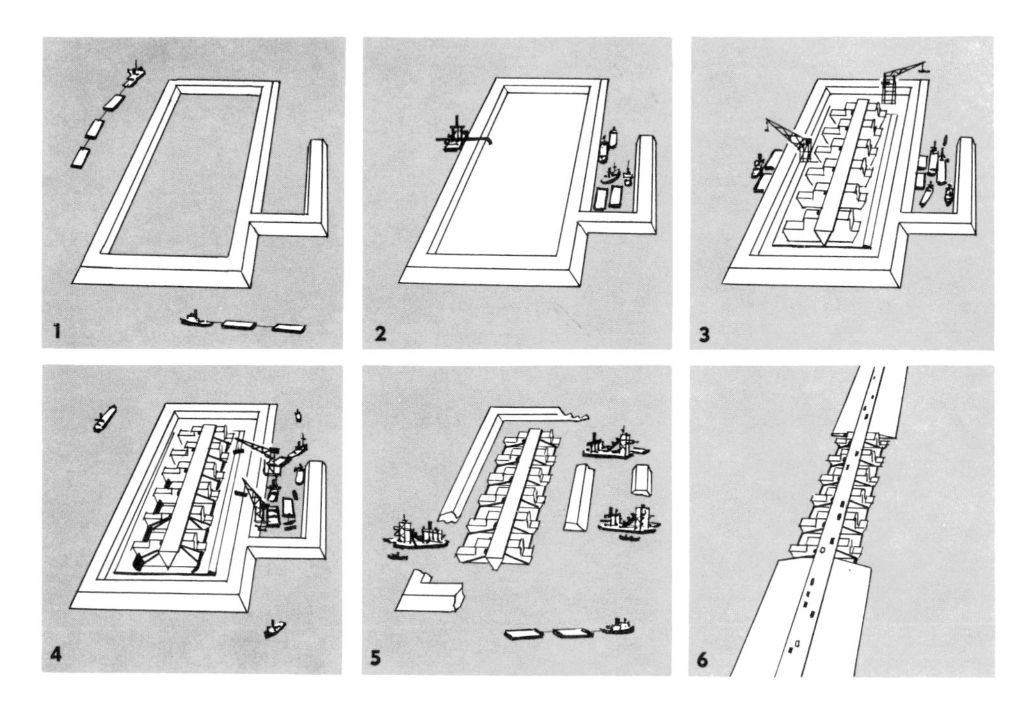

How the Haringvliet's building pit, "the island in reverse," was made. The same method is used to construct locks and caisson pits. 1. Ringdike and harbor are built. 2. Water is pumped out. 3. Sluice bed, piers and spans are constructed. 4. Steel gates and hydraulic machinery are fitted. 5. Dredges remove dikes. 6. Connecting dams are built on both sides.

Some of the inlets will be spanned by cable ways from which fast, self-propelled cars will be able to dump ten-ton loads into the sea. Because precision and speed are essential, barges capable of dumping 160 tons of stone in a few minutes were built.

Another innovation is the "building pit," an "island in reverse." Since it takes a great deal of time to build the special sluice complexes and pumping stations that have to be ready to go into operation the instant a new dike is closed, work on them has to be started long before the building of the dike itself. A great ringdike is built in the middle of the water on the future site of the new installation, and the water is pumped out of it. This leaves a dry "island" on the bottom of the sea, in which the construction can begin. The ringdike is removed when the main dike is finished. The caissons, too, are built as close to their final destination as possible in special dock pits.

This is the Delta Plan timetable:

1 Stormflood barrage in Hollandse IJssel, finished 1958.
2 Dike and shipping locks across Zandkreek, finished 1960.
3 Dike across Veere Gap, finished 1961.

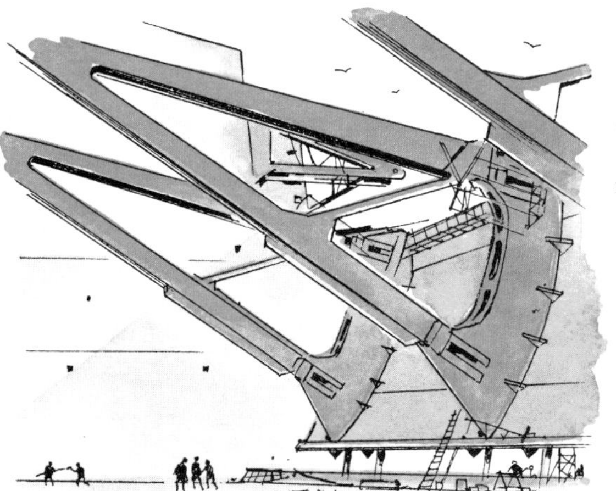

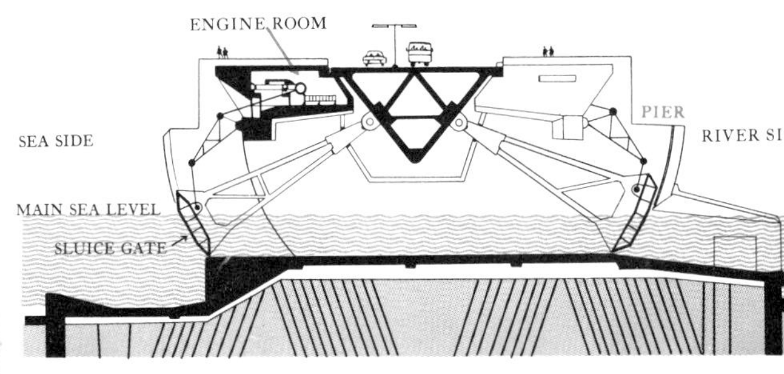

Inside a Haringvliet sluice before inundation. Section of sluice: 28,000 concrete piles securely anchor the complex in place. Each gate weighs 500 tons!

4 Grevelingen dike and locks, finished 1965.
5 Volkerak dikes, locks, inlet sluices and bridges, finished 1970.
6 Haringvliet dike, locks, bridges, and sluices, finished 1971.

The huge outlet slucies in the Haringvliet dike are unlike any seen before: a row of seventeen fully automated sluices, with a combined length of 1092 yards and more than 300 feet wide! Each sluice gate has its own engine room and the whole complex is fully automated with computers and data-processing machines that are fed hydraulic and meteorological data which determine when—and how far—the steel doors must open and close.

This installation is of the greatest importance. It acts as a safety valve to let the water from Rhine, Meuse, Waal, and Lek flow to the sea. In winter this is especially vital to allow a free passage to the abundance of ice coming downstream.

7 Brouwershaven dike, finished 1972.
8 Dike across Easter Scheldt, finished 1978.

On Monday, April 24, 1961, the last culvert caisson was edged in place in the Veere dike. The Queen and many important Dutchmen were there in the royal yacht. The shores were lined with spectators from all over the country and flags flew from every mast. When that caisson settled on its prepared foundations, all hell broke loose. Two giant suction dredgers immediately began pumping 4000 cubic yards of sand into the top level of the caisson, which was the size of a junior

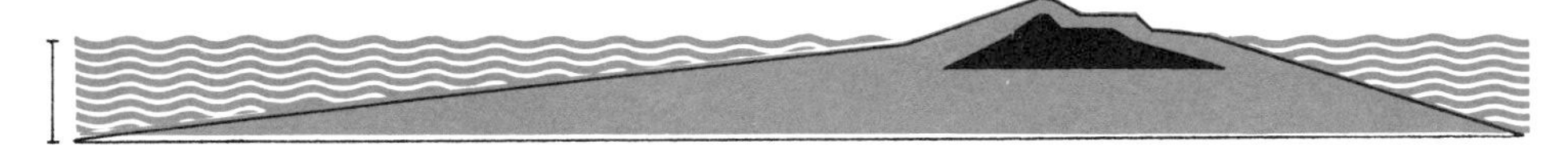

A cross section of the Zuiderzee Enclosing dike (1932) shown within a section of the Easter Scheldt dam (1978).

One of 17 pairs of sluice gates, each 180 feet wide (above). They are so large, that, if river-ice floes block the gates, an icebreaker attacking the obstruction can ram its way to the sea, passing underneath the raised gates. The last remnants of the building pit ringdike are dredged away (below).

Veerse Gat –
Veerse Gat –
Lauwerszee – Oost Mahorn –68.

city block. Divers and workmen hastily plugged leaks and reinforced the bottom of the sea floor on the sides of the caisson, for the incoming tide began to wash away the sand underneath the sill of the seven concrete mastodons. For three more days the tides thundered through the openings in the caissons, which finally slammed shut when the tide was dead low on April 27.

Then the dike was finished with modern materials, and on October 27 the road across the dike was officially opened. It was a great day!

The Dutch, as if they do not yet have enough work on their hands with the Zuiderzee Works and their Delta Project far from finished, have also started building service harbors and sluice pits in the Lauwerszee, the bay lying between Friesland and Groningen. The plans for the Lauwerszee Project were incorporated into the Delta Laws. It will be finished in 1970, and the eight-mile-long dike will improve water control in the three northern provinces—much to the joy of the farmers and the townspeople as well, because the old sea dike was no longer

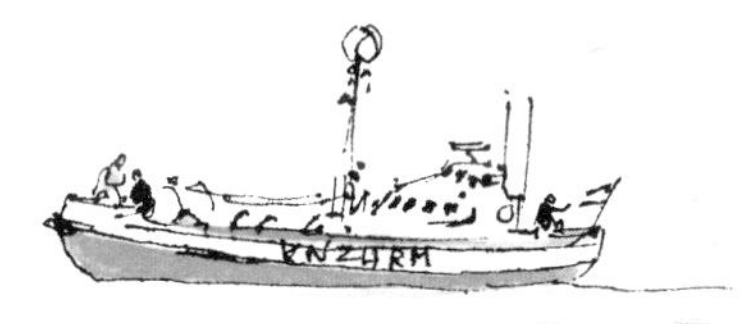

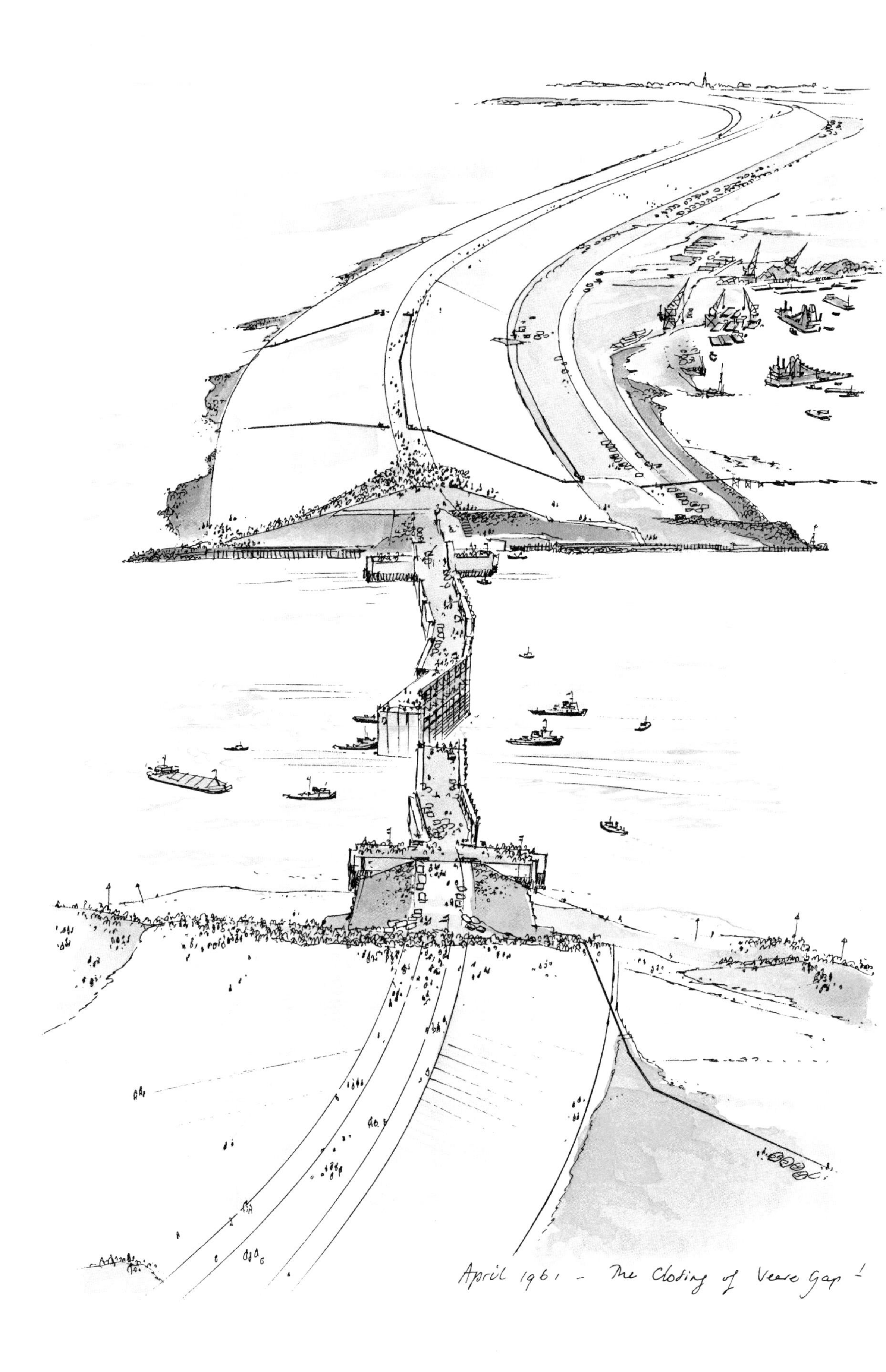
April 1961 - The Closing of Veere Gap!

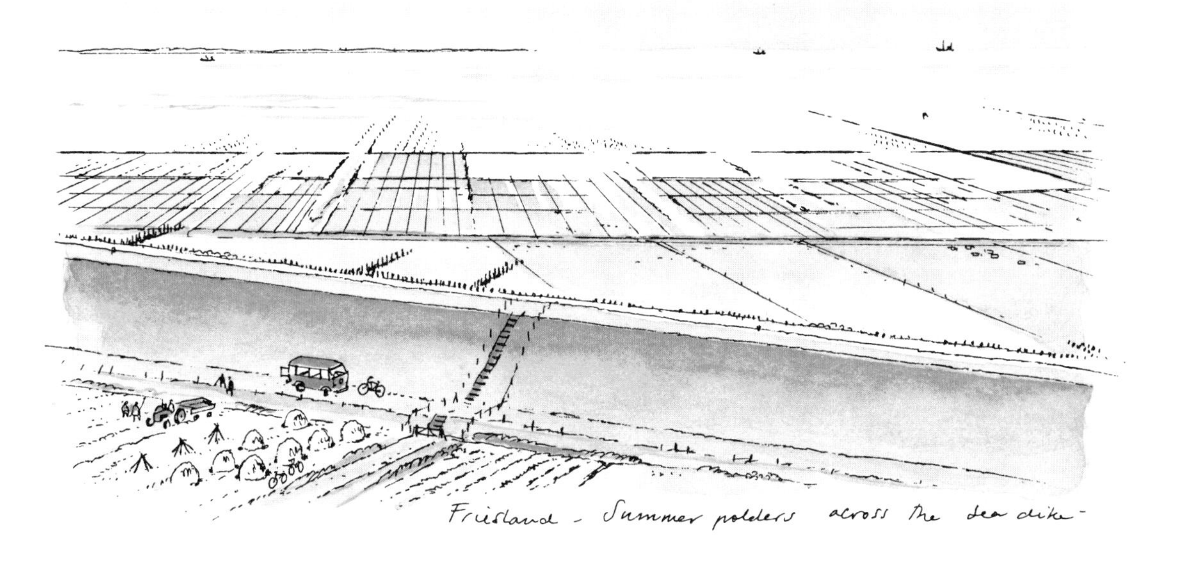

Friesland - Summer polders across the sea dike -

considered high enough or strong enough. But, as always, tempers flared when the work was begun. The shrimp fishermen fought the plan desperately, for the water in the Lauwerszee is a few degrees warmer than that of the North Sea and is therefore a perfect breeding ground of the shrimp.

"The Frisians are cowards," said Skipper van Wierda, a shrimp fisherman who was quite obviously historically not well informed. "They are so scared that they go to bed wearing life jackets!"

Shortly before the nineteenth century ended, a wealthy man built a dike from the Frisian coast to Ameland, counting on the sea to deposit silt against his dike. Around this silt he planned to build another dike so that he would have a valuable private polder. Alas, he should not have counted on the sea. He discovered that he was not nearly rich enough for the undertaking. His dike soon needed repairs—which he could not afford—and then the sea made short work of it. Not a trace of it is left today.

Getting something for nothing has always been a most appealing proposition, and the Dutch like it just as much as anybody else. (Some say even more.) It was the sea that kept adding silt and clay particles to the land around the terpen, and man protected this gift with a dike. From the earliest days man has done all he could to stimulate the sea's generosity.

In 1925 an English grass (*Spartina townsendii*) was imported; it thrived in sea water, its leaves held on to silt, and it was extensively used in Zeeland to add land outside the dikes and in other shallow areas.

New land also grew on the sea side of the Frisian and Groningen dikes in the Wadden Sea. Here the inhabitants had always encouraged the silt

The relatively easy center section of the Brouwershaven dam was finished and the towers for the aerial railway were in place. "Self-propelled cable cars can work night and day, are not really affected by wind or waves and drop 10 tons of stone from the net slung below the cab," said the man from Waterstaat. "They'll drop 225,000 tons for a start. It's calm today, but these 1000 yards are going to be tough: 90 feet deep and a current that tops 5 feet a second!" The battle had already begun. 11:15 A.M., low tide: two tugs moved a sinker piece in position. 11:30: a self-unloading barge was maneuvered across the mattress. The sound of distant thunder rolled over the water as 300 tons of stone were dumped from the barge. 11:36: The mattress slowly sank to the bottom.

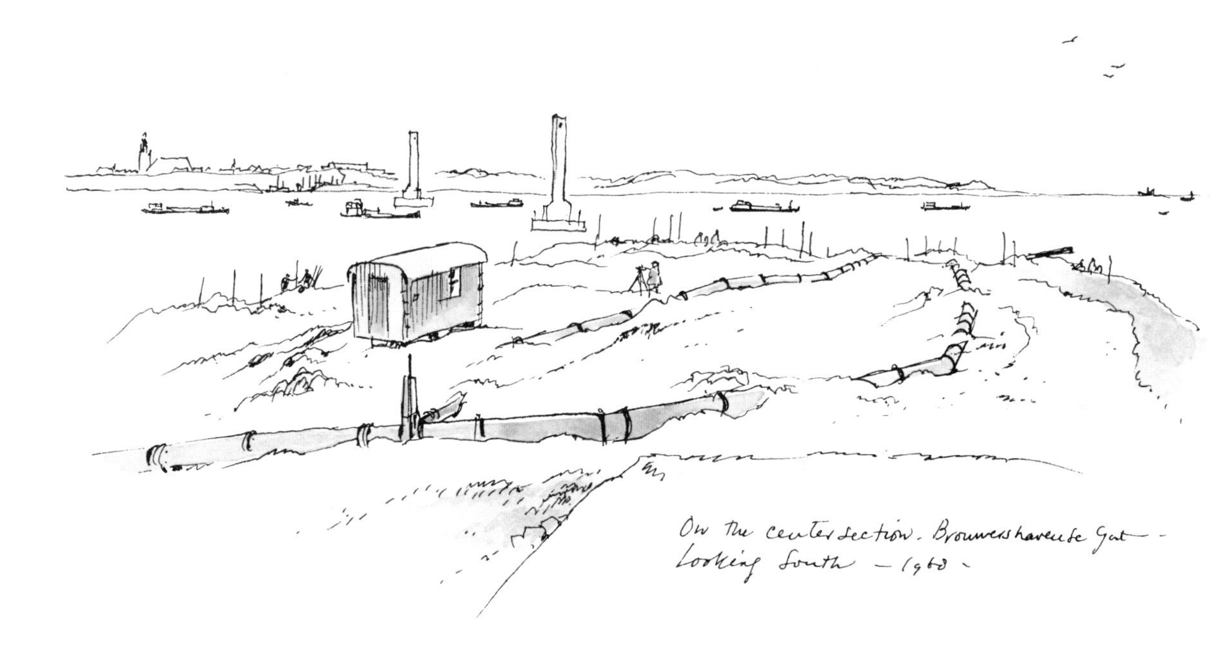

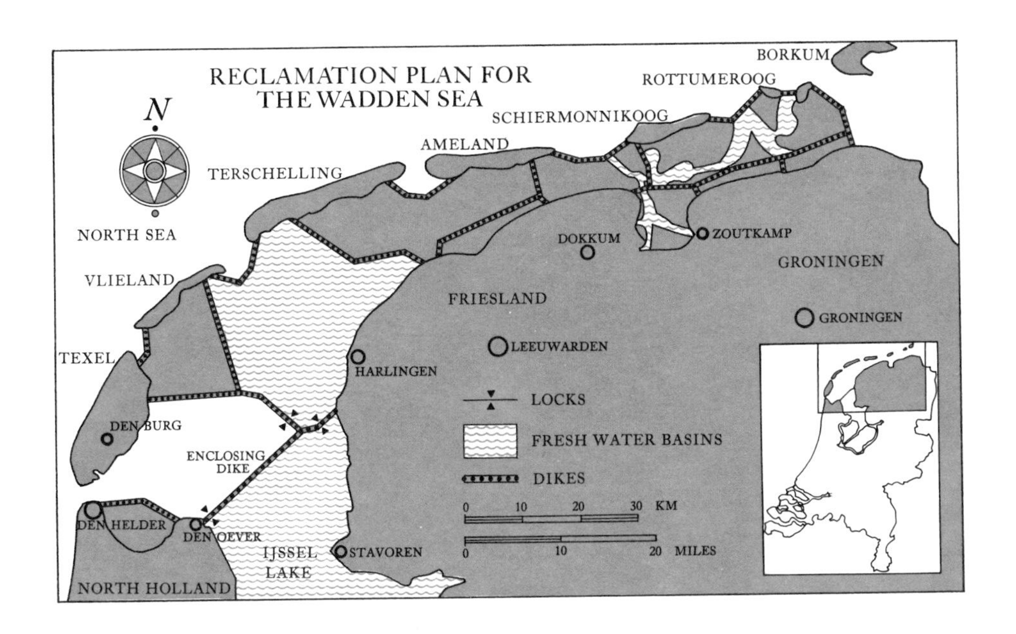

to settle by digging trenches at straight angles to the incoming tide. In 1936 this was improved on by adding low ridges, in the top of which twigs and reeds were stuck, slowing down the eroding water movement. This is by no means a pastime for the impatient, since even with luck it takes a full year to accumulate the better part of an inch, and a minimum layer of two feet is needed to grow anything useful. Still, it has been done for years and these summer polders—so called because they are usually flooded in winter—have been growing at a snail's pace, but growing nevertheless.

So it is only natural—for the Dutch, that is!—to be eying the Wadden Sea, that wild, treacherous piece of water—crisscrossed with ever-changing gullies and channels—between the islands and the top of Holland. Plans are being made to reclaim it and part of the diked-in Lauwers Sea will become a test polder like the one built in the Zuiderzee. On a few Dutch hydraulic maps there are some faint outlines drawn in the Wadden Sea and the tiny light blue label reads, "To be completed in the distant future." It will in all probability be done in the twenty-first century.

And after that? Will they ever stop dredging and draining, will they ever quit building new dikes and pumping sand and clay? No. Not very likely. Not they. As long as there is a bucket of water left in the sea, the Dutch will try to dike it in and turn it into land!

"Nature has undoubtedly passed a fixed decree that Holland shall be completely lost, for it has not given you the means of renewing yourselves!" James Boswell once told a Dutch officer. I'd say Boswell was wrong. It may have been what Nature intended, but the mound dwellers and their descendants decided otherwise!

Index

(*Map references are italicized*)

About the Author

Peter Spier is probably best known for his illustrations for children's books. His *The Fox Went Out on a Chilly Night* was a runner-up for the Caldecott Medal, and the first two books in his widely acclaimed Mother Goose Library, *London Bridge Is Falling Down* and *To Market! To Market!,* were winner and runner-up respectively for the Boston *Globe*–Horn Book Award. But in OF DIKES AND WINDMILLS his admirers will discover a new talent. He is a master storyteller.

Born and educated in Amsterdam, Mr. Spier came to New York in 1952 after serving in the Royal Dutch Navy and working for a number of years as a reporter for *Elsevier's Weekly,* Holland's largest weekly magazine. He has illustrated more than seventy-five books and has also contributed a series of murals to the Winterthur Museum in Delaware.

Mr. Spier, who is now a United States citizen, lives in Port Washington, Long Island, with his wife and two children, where, in addition to illustrating, he sails and, on rainy days, builds ship models.